A HOUSE CALLED MEMORY

BY RICHARD COLLIER

A HOUSE
CALLED MEMORY

By RICHARD COLLIER

E. P. DUTTON & COMPANY, INC.

NEW YORK   1961

To the memory of
my mother and father

CONTENTS

LOOKING BACK

And lo! my infancy is gone long since, and yet I live!
CONFESSIONS OF ST. AUGUSTINE

WHEN THE last car had gone, printing its tyres deep in the moss of the drive, then came one of the hardest decisions that ever I had to make.

For here was the house, still square above valley and farm and church spire, where my father had built it, and here was I, seeming silent and alone in it, save for the rush and swish of tap-water downstairs, where they washed the purple rinsings from the wine-glasses and brushed the funeral crumbs from Minton plates.

To fly from this house of memory, where I had not lived for so long, or to stay? I beseeched God for guidance then, because I did not know.

To go, I had said all that morning, while the cruel wind strove with the topmost branches of the elms and the rain and the driblets of earth beat their threnody on the polished oak of the coffin and the parson, not relishing the rain and wind, gabbled my mother's orisons as fast as decency would allow: " Man-that-is-born-of-woman "—the wind teasing at the india-paper of the Prayer Book—" has-but-a-short-time-to-live." And the grief for my mother was a cold, coiled lump where my belly should have been : my mother, gone now to join my father.

Rain drenched the mourners and the lovely painted blooms ; the priest departed with flapping of surplice. All over now.

I shook hands with decent people, all in black, not hearing their words. In little groups they moved to their cars, and somewhere a bell tolled. You could see people buying groceries in the High Street over the wall, the High Street that was open fields when I was a boy.

To go, said my heart with the tolling of the bell. *To go*.

But that afternoon, watching the valley, with the storm of grief spent a little, I wondered. Had it been meant to end like this—a " For Sale " board in red and black under the laburnum tree, people to whom the house was just wood and brick, testing each floorboard, coldly critical of cupboard space, an eyebrow arched at the broken stair-rod my father would never mend ? Or was I to return here, slave to the rich memories of the past?

All my wealth was in those memories. And I need only look from any window to see that more than the wealth of the mind was needed here.

All in a few years my father's garden lay in ruins, reclaimed by the farmland from which he so painfully fashioned it. Thick cushions of chickweed quilted the kitchen garden and couch-grass sprouted rank on the tennis-court that no gardener was ever trusted to mow. The garden gate through which my father had sauntered each evening was pulpy with the rain of many winters, and the syringa bushes bordering the drive bulged brokenly, unpruned these years past.

Here, once my father had died, my mother lived and waited for death, and the feel of death was upon this house, in its walls that sweated damp, in its tarnished mirrors, and in the rain-bowed grasses of its garden.

Could I work to restore it to what it once had been ? I believed I could. Yet why, when, in the end, I had no heirs ? Wouldn't some flat or furnished cottage better suit my purpose ? How much tribute did the past demand ?

All the voices that I knew—friends, wisdom distilled from books—said *Go*. " No man bathes twice in the same river." You cannot recapture the past ; you cannot preserve it, frail yet still intact, like a wasp's nest plucked from the hedgerow. All over England people were giving up such houses and gardens, retrenching, acknowledging the present.

Someone else could buy this house, someone who could afford to restore it, for whom it held no memories. I would sign the conveyance and to him I would deliver my memories, neatly parcelled, with the freehold. It would be logical and unsentimental. It made crystal-clear economic sense.

Then what held me back and tortured me with doubts? Was it a yearning for the security of childhood and the morning of my life, a time before the corruption of innocence? Or was it a belief, cherished despite the tide of progress engulfing us, the contempt for so much that was past, that man must preserve as well as build anew?

And this house was the symbol of things worth preserving, of all that was a living truth inside me.

This book is the story of how it came to be. History was being made as the memories grew, but no historic events had us for players, for this was a happy time. Few deaths are recorded in my chronicle, no thrones topple, nobody faces irretrievable ruin. Its sole justification is to tell what it was like to grow up in a country house in the south of England thirty years ago, since that, too, has its niche in history.

For the world in which the house and I grew up together is dead and will not come back again.

CHAPTER ONE

AN AGE OF RITUAL

Custom reconciles us to everything

EDMUND BURKE

OUR DAY always began with a key grating in the back door downstairs, followed by the snap of the light switch in the kitchen. Then we knew that Lucy had arrived to start work on the shoes.

From the time that I slept in a cot in my parents' room until just before the outbreak of the Second World War, I can never remember a day that did not begin like that.

What a business, the shoe-cleaning in those days! I suppose most people clean their own shoes now, one pair at a time as needed, and make a fair job of it, too, but when I was a boy shoe-cleaning was as much a ritual as a necessity. It was almost an affirmation that you had shoes to *be* cleaned, as immutable as a barrack-room inspection.

Out would come the soft yellow dusters, and the big bristled brushes, both soft and hard, the suède cleaners, the pots of cream and the three different kinds of polish. Next, every pair of shoes in the house would be solemnly ranged on the kitchen floor. Then, while the kettle boiled for my father's shaving water, Lucy set to work.

Presently there would be two rituals taking place at one and the same time—the shoe-cleaning and my father's shaving. All this at seven o'clock in the morning, for people started early and took their time.

When I was about four, I worked out a compromise to enjoy the full flavour of both these rituals. I would wait until my father had rasped the last blob of lather from his chin and then tumble downstairs to the kitchen. That was always a sight worth seeing—a dozen or more pairs of shoes, from my father's brogues to my mother's best blue calf and in between all the ebonies and chocolates and nigger browns, winking and gleaming under the harsh yellow light as only good leather can. And over it all, the smell of polish and boiling milk.

Then Lucy would look up from her kneeling-mat by the wood-box, brush a wisp of hair from her face and say, " 'Morning, Master Dickie—are you a good boy to-day ? "

Mostly I wasn't, being given to silent solo forays which ended in the upsetting of coal scuttles or the collapse of frail occasional tables, and the dignity of four years recoiled from the diminutive implications of " Master Dickie." But I liked Lucy, our gardener's daughter, sensing with the animal sympathy of the very young that she was often tired and overworked and that at thirty-five marriage was unlikely to rid her of the necessity of working for us. So often I would help her to put the shoes away.

Yes, the shoes were now put away—for though no one could wear more than one pair of shoes at a time, all of them were carefully polished each day and then reverently replaced in the boot rack behind a discreet blue curtain.

But first came the shaving.

I never saw any other man shave like my father, though most fathers were the same from what I heard. There were no electric razors or dry-shavers then, and even safety-razors weren't much used. To-day I can shave in seven minutes flat, yet it took my father the best part of half an hour.

Selecting the razor was the first part of the ceremony. Why my father kept half a dozen razors in the compactum in his dressing-room, I never knew; perhaps most men did then. Royal United Services razors, they were, made by Turner's of Sheffield, the old cut-throat kind with ebony handles and the royal crest stamped in gold on each of them. And my father kept each blade packed in vaseline, so that whichever razor he used, the clinging yellow grease had to be wiped from it first.

Then my father would adjust the leather strop that hung on his dressing-room door and hone that razor till it had an edge like an east wind.

Up came the shaving water, piping hot in a high necked, enamel jug, to be poured little by little into a big china mug, like the kind old-fashioned barbers use, with a generous niche to hold the lather. That was one of the parts I liked best—to see my father use brush and hot water and shaving soap to beat the lather into a thick fine froth like the whipped cream in a cake.

When the lather was just right, and my father had plastered it so liberally on his chin that he looked like Santa Claus, then was the time to hold your breath. Then the word went down to Lucy that " the master had started," so that she and all of us would walk on pins, in case some unlooked-for clatter should startle my father into cutting his throat. Very uncomfortable he looked shaving, with his head tilted to one side, as if he had dislocated his neck, using the fingers of his left hand to keep the skin of his cheeks taut, but at least his shaving was a process independent of bathroom or bustle. None of your bathroom cabinet mirrors with a tiny square of glass like a peep-hole for my father, but a special shaving stand on a tripod by the dressing-room fire, with a mounted swivel mirror that you could adjust to any angle, the boiling water standing ready on what must have been the showpiece of my father's dressing-room—the marble-topped wash-stand of grey-green walnut, chilly with its ewers and jugs and soap dishes.

To me it was magic to see how that blade slid down his jaw coated with cream, and, before the next stroke, every daub of lather carefully cleaned from the blade with little strips of newspaper that Lucy had cut for the purpose. And at the end of it all there was the blade to be cleaned again, packed in more vaseline and returned to its presentation case.

Of course, there was the sensation of all time stretching before you then, supporting the logic of such rituals. By the time my father had shaved, bathed and dressed—that is, selected a shirt and links and a stiff white collar and disposed the gleaming gold of his watch-chain across his waistcoat—he must have been out of bed fully an hour, and even then had not breakfasted.

There may have been more speed in some households, but never in ours. My father had married late in life and I had come later still so that he was past forty-five at the time I am writing about. A senior controller of the British Board of Trade, he was by that time, and thinking not about saving time but about savouring each passing moment to the full. So you may be sure there was truth in it when my mother said, as she often did, " You'll never hurry any Collier—least of all your father."

My father was a dark man of medium height, with a sensitive mouth that crinkled with laughter more often than with anger. His eyes were grey and sometimes when he was laughing or truly moved by something they seemed almost blue behind his steel-rimmed spectacles. He was a tolerant, peaceful man with a passionate sense of justice, as dependent as I was on my mother's practical presence, but the one thing you could not do was hasten the pace of his life. He said it disturbed his train of thought.

" I can't be hurried," I heard him say, time and again, " and I won't be hurried."

So while my mother cooked breakfast for us and for Lucy my father would always step forth to cast a squire's proud eye over his house and garden.

I think he had good reason to be proud, looking back. Almost twenty years before, as a clerk earning £50 a year, he had seen this land, mild green pasture on a hilltop above a valley where red Alderney cattle cropped gently in fly-haunted grass, and the villagers from the small hamlet nearby came wandering in search of mushrooms. And, one day, my father swore, he would make this his home, but it was not until 1924, ten years after he had married my mother, that he could muster £1300 to buy an acre of it and build a house, though he bought another half acre soon after that. This second half acre he bought in case someone

" overlooked " us. Nothing galled the men of my father's generation more than being " overlooked."

But of course the building of the house came long before the planning of the garden.

It was like a Tudor house in some ways, except that it had no zebra timbering or leaded windows or any of the shams just then so fashionable. Just plain cream plaster and good brick with a gable overhung by chimneys, a big bow window for the dining-room that caught the morning sun and wide windows everywhere, even french windows from house to lawn. I shall always remember those windows and the way the house seemed at times like a prism, so that you bathed in sun like an animal : sun striking through the bars of a cot, sun swamping the high chair by the breakfast table in a flood of honeyed light, sun upon the black wool rug where at the age of four I passed all my day, grunting industriously with crayons to colour newspaper advertisements of Mansion Polish and Hovis and Keatings Powder.

The house was well-planned inside, with plenty of cupboard space, and three bedrooms, and a tiled kitchen, and that, in its way, was a miracle, since my father, with a touching faith that the builder would " do his duty like an English gentleman," only visited the house twice during the course of construction. So the house was well enough planned on paper but there were faults in plenty in brickwork and tiling, and the weather and the years were not slow to find them out.

As to the furnishings, they were in the fashion of the day, and you might say that every house across the valley was fitted out on much the same lines. All the furniture and the fittings were of dark oak with yards of highly-polished oak boards— more work for Lucy who somehow managed to work over them each day with a tin of Ronuk polish and a wealth of rags. Cushions and chair-covers all in spinach green, French purple rugs to set them off, sepia-tinted family groups everywhere, on the mantelpiece, on the piano, on my father's special smoking-cabinet, and bronze vases filled with Cape gooseberries wherever you cared to look.

And if not much of that would be to our taste to-day it was just the natural setting of a happy home then, as much a part of it as the brass and the pictures.

For above all things my father prized simplicity as a virtue and to him that meant not only polished oak but enough glowing highly-polished brass to do credit to a fire-station : brass fire irons, brass cauldrons, brass curtain-rods, brass ash-trays, brass candlesticks and ornaments. Much the same with the pictures, too, for people liked their art as they liked their meals—something solid you could sink your teeth into. All of them were suspended on long cords from oaken picture-rails and they were of two kinds : a few water-colours of harbour scenes and church spires that my father had admired on cycle trips while courting my mother and many mighty gilt-framed reproductions that belonged to an older world. So we had " The Laughing Cavalier " above the umbrella stand, " The Fighting Temeraire " looming over the old upright telephone, and all the ones you might expect, including one whose name I never knew. A girl weeping over a dead spaniel was its subject and it hung square on the landing so that the first and last thing you saw, rising or going to bed, was the whites of her eyes fairly rolling in grief.

If all this seems more like Edwardian times than the nineteen-twenties, remember that that age was only seventeen years away, and we were closer to it in spirit than we are now to the days of my youth. Habit and custom decided almost everything—even the pictures. I don't believe my parents were any happier about the spaniel than I was but many of the pictures had hung in their own homes and passed down as heirlooms, so that it was a kind of link with tradition to have them hanging there still.

Even breakfast was a routine that did not vary. My father's digestion was never robust, yet his conviction that fried bacon and tomato was the finest breakfast an Englishman could tackle overrode everything. I can see him now, his eyes gleaming with enthusiasm over pink chunky slices of well-cooked gammon piled with golden-red tomatoes ; that diet was unchanging from year to year, as much a part of my father as his watch-chain or his shaving. For it didn't stop short at breakfast ; at lunch-time he

17

would leave his Westminster office, in the shadow of the Abbey, and board a bus for Holborn, twenty minutes away, because a restaurant there had it on the menu. Of course, that wasn't the only one; he had his bacon-and-tomato restaurants and pubs all over the city, so it wasn't surprising that my mother's recipe book was filled with suggestions clipped from cookery columns that were never followed up. For three meals out of five bacon and tomatoes always won.

Breakfast over, there would be another little ceremony. My father would lean back in his chair, apply a napkin to his lips and remark, "I must be off like a shot from a yeoman's bow." But no great evidence of haste followed this announcement. Instead my father filled one of several well-worn briar pipes and smoked it to the end, checked his watch by the dining-room clock and wound it, and went out, with a knowing look, to tap the ornate carved barometer in the hall. Finally, at some time after half past eight, he would bend over and give me a kiss smelling of tea, tobacco and shaving soap. Then, a rose perked in his buttonhole, his ankles snug in spats, high-crowned grey trilby hat on his head and cane twirling, he would stroll off through the gate to a mysterious world twenty miles away called "Office." And when I was young that, for twenty-four hours, would be the last I saw of him.

So most of my day centred round my mother and Lucy and sometimes round old Mr. Wade, Lucy's father, a ruddy-cheeked, ponderous old man, with waxed sergeant-major moustaches who was helping my father convert the surrounding meadowland into a garden.

I soon found out that as an only child I had to spend a lot of time on my own. Not that I ever minded solitude, especially in summer, for I got used to it early, and there is nothing more pleasant than your own thoughts on a summer's morning, even the aimless, shapeless thoughts that you think in a play-pen under the beech trees, with the jungle of thick meadow-grass all round and the grey squirrel chiding from the topmost branches and sometimes, a shrew, tiny and dun-coloured, flashing from one patch of grass to the next to leave a drifting shower of yellow pollen in its wake. You are part of the peace of that world, like an animal drowsing in the sun, and all the noise going on in the house, the beating and banging and burnishing, ruffles you like it ruffles an animal.

For my mother and Lucy had their ritual too, one which never stopped. Each hour was an Hour and each day a Day, fixed, unchanging. Monday, of course, was washing day, when great zinc tubs of water boiled on the gas-stove from nine in the morning to well beyond four in the afternoon. And all the time the kitchen walls sweated steam and the big iron mangle squealed protestingly and above the plot of grass where the daffodils blazed golden in springtime the washing flapped in relays on the line like a windjammer under sail. For if washing machines and spin dryers were unknown, there were whole chests-of-drawers packed with linen, and every meal called for starched damask table-cloths and napkins, every bed had its linen bed-spread and almost every plate used at tea seemed to need a doily. No wonder that lunch on Monday was always cold meat and pickles to avoid, as my mother said, " a palaver about food."

Tuesday was Ironing Day, when you could hardly move through the kitchen for a peep at what might be in the larder for all the mounds of warm snowy linen piled everywhere—and remember every inch of it was smoothed with a flat-iron, which was brought red-hot from the embers of the boiler and gingerly fitted into a metal case. And as the week began, so it went on. Wednesday was Cupboard Day, when either the linen cupboard or the china cupboard or the larder would be turned inside out and scrubbed with carbolic soap and the contents washed or refolded before the shelves were relined with clean white paper and everything put back again. Next came Brass Day, and finally, on Friday, Silver Day, when enough cutlery and teapots and salvers to equip a caterer's, wedding presents most of them, were delicately unwrapped from green baize bags called " butlers " and burnished with Goddard's Plate Powder.

Yet for all our labour-saving devices it often seems to me that my mother had more leisure than most mothers have to-day. Each morning at eleven she would pay a visit to the small parade of shops that stood under the pinewood in the lee of the railway station, and that in itself was a thing to see. There was no question then of her slipping on a coat and going just as she was. First she would go upstairs to her bedroom and change from a house-dress into a tailored costume, complete with a good silk blouse, a fur stole, smart town shoes and a snugly-fitting cloche hat set on her brown shingled hair. I was never more proud of her than when, dressed up like that, she went forth, drawing on clean white gloves and carrying an umbrella or a parasol according to the weather, to visit the tradesmen and place her orders.

The one thing that she never took with her was a shopping basket, for it was " not done " to carry back your own meat or groceries. So the only thing my mother took with her were her order-books. You almost never see them to-day, those dark red or dark blue linen-bound books, the size and shape of passports, with the shopkeeper's name and something high-flown like " Purveyor of High-Class Provisions " stamped in gold leaf on the front. Inside them the tradesmen noted down your orders —it was " not done " to write down your own—and perhaps once a month you presented the book, together with a cheque, to be receipted. In a way, I suppose, they *were* passports, for they affirmed the owner's status as a housewife of means, blessed with a credit account—since it was " not done " to pay cash down. Her orders placed, my mother might adjourn with her friends to the old oak and chequered table-cloths of the Willow Tea Rooms, and before she was even home again those orders might have been delivered by any one of the five errand-boys who daily thundered at our back door.

They used to worry me, those errand-boys. You saw them everywhere then, and when a tradesman hung a " Smart Lad Wanted " sign in his window, there was never any lack of response. In our village, to be an errand-boy at fourteen was as much a vocation for lads as going into service was for girls like Lucy, unless, of course, the boy had a taste for farm work and could guide the heads of the big brown Clydesdales as they ploughed the five-acre field which sloped up the valley opposite our bedroom windows. No ploughing by tractor then! Either way, it was a dead-end life for most of them, but outside the towns there were few factories : what else could they do ? And yet they worried me. Many of them came from the poorest homes in the village, where the women were hard put to it to buy the food to keep their men going. I knew all the errand boys when I was growing up, and even then I sensed something was wrong.

I remember once toddling to the back door in a white knitted-suit to ask the fishmonger's lad my favourite question, " What did you have for breakfast to-day ? "

He was a tousle-haired, ruddy-cheeked lad wearing a cloth cap too big for him, with a whistle as piercing as a factory siren. But when I asked him this he grinned sheepishly, ill-at-ease, shifting his weight from one great boot to the other.

Finally he mumbled, " 'Ad bread pullet."

Now this started a train of discovery. First I had to find my mother and ask her, " What's a pullet ? " A pullet was a young hen. Well, how could you make one out of bread ? " You can't, dear, don't be silly." Well, the boy who brought the fish could, anyway. He'd had it for breakfast. He said so. But for once my mother, who I firmly believed knew everything, was out of her depth. Plainly she'd never heard of " bread pullet."

I taxed Lucy. It was obvious that she knew, but obvious, too, that she didn't want to go into too many details. It was something to eat, very nice, she'd had it herself at times. And I didn't want to go worrying my head with things like that. Without knowing it, I was committing the unforgivable sin of prying into the private life of the poor. But what I did know was that there was a conspiracy afoot to prevent me plumbing the mystery of " bread pullet."

They should have known better. For the next few weeks tradesmen, cultivated ladies at my mother's tea parties, even total strangers in the lane were startled to find a determined four-year-old accosting them without ceremony to demand the precise nature of " bread pullet." Finally my mother did some investigating on her own account and discovered that it was a kind of bread pudding eaten with gravy. This, I was told, and told also to stop worrying strangers.

But this only intrigued me further. If it was just bread, did the fishmonger's lad eat it with bacon and tomato? No, it was probable he just ate it on its own. But why? Didn't he like bacon and tomato? You couldn't just eat *bread*. Finally it had to be said, " Some people are very poor, dear—they just can't afford anything better for breakfast."

Well, that I *could* understand. But something was wrong somewhere—I could understand that too.

Close though I was to my mother, closer than to my father, who for long periods I did not see, this is really the place to write of Lucy. I was closer to her at four than I could ever be again, and so closest to this world of " bread pullet " that I would never otherwise have known.

I have never been so close to it again. Try how you may, there are barriers that will stand in the way and prevent a perfect understanding. It was different when I was four. I sensed that our ways of life were different, right enough, but there was no feeling of constraint. All my values were absolute : Lucy, and so many like her, were my good friends. I liked them better than most of the people who came to tea.

I rarely left Lucy's side. As much as anything, I think, that sense of difference fascinated me. Lucy did not smell, like my mother did, of perfume or toilet water, but mostly of polish or washing-soda, and Hudson's soap, for it seems, looking back, that Lucy was always polishing or scrubbing something. So many brooms and brushes and rags and carpet-sweepers were involved in Lucy's war against dirt that the cupboard under the stairs was dedicated to these alone. So Lucy's hands, unlike my mother's, were not a delicate flesh colour but chapped and red, the nails split and cracked. I never saw her hair waved or set, only scraped back and held in place by a comb. The only really attractive thing about her was her eyes, which were a warm brown, and I loved her.

Poor Lucy ! Sometimes it seems that for a wage of ten shillings a week we exploited her shamefully, though it was the standard wage for the time. I don't even know how you could define her duties, for as in so many households that could then only afford one servant, she was a daily woman until lunch-time, a nursemaid in the afternoon and a parlour-maid, complete with cap and apron (provided) if my mother had a tea-party. And she was happier than most girls with her post! My mother was easygoing, let her do things her own way in her own time, fed her three good meals a day, for she was never one to stint and talked to her like a human being. Not that Lucy ever replied with much more than a " Yes, m'm," or a " No, m'm," but she was probably too tired. She was with us from seven in the morning until after six at night, and after that she had to walk a mile through dark leafy lanes back to the village.

Yet never a Christmas went by during the war without a card from Lucy, anxious to know how things went. Each time it came I would remember so much and wonder if she remembered too. Did she remember those walks of ours, almost every after-noon from two-thirty to four ? The walks down the lane to the dairy, swinging the enamelled milk jug, to watch Miss Milne, who wore the same black felt hat like an upturned coal scuttle all the years I knew her, slapping the butter into deft little pats on the cold stone slab. And the walks to the grocery store, shelves piled high with black-and-gold japanned jars of pepper and cinnamon and sago, its inside dark and smelling of apples and matches and paraffin and tea and the smoky tang of bacon as the slicer cut into it. Or the summer walks, when the grass on the heath under the birch trees shone like fine green hair in the sun and long imaginary " telephone conversations " could be conducted with the aid of frail blue hairbells. The winter walks, when the wind soughed through the branches of the wood, the leaves a trodden carpet of umber underfoot, each puddle shining like a steel mirror.

But it was the people, rather than the scenery, that counted most. My parents loved the country, their values in many ways were country values yet I think I learned much that would have surprised them. I don't think they ever knew that Lucy had an uncanny way with animals, so that rabbits would play within ten feet of her, or that she liked organ music best, because it made her cry, or that she went to the village church each Sunday and believed every word that was preached. This was Lucy's world, for her values were her father's values, transmitted long years since and never questioned.

I came closest to them sometimes when she took me home to the cottage where she lived with her parents, with its tiny kitchen garden and its earth closet " out back " and its doll's-house windows. There, in a house as dim and crowded as an antique shop, I would first watch with fascination while old Mr. Wade sluiced his hairy forearms, all bruised blue with tattoos, at the kitchen sink, smelling the pleasant slightly sweet smell of earth and sweat and fresh grass that was always about him. Then, by the white light of a globe oil-lamp, he would settle down in the parlour at a table covered with a velvet cloth, tuck a napkin in his neck above a gleaming brass collar stud and wolf cold steak-and-kidney pie in his shirtsleeves. No " bread pullet " you see, for old Mr. Wade, passing rich on the fifty shillings we paid him every week.

I remember that a bright bank of coals always burned in the fireplace and that there was a bobbled velvet mantel fringe, with sepia photographs of Mr. Wade, in a pill-box hat worn sideways on his head like a page-boy, as a sergeant-major in the Boer War. And I thought, how much more fun this was than sitting in the dining-room at home picking a protesting way through boiled fish.

Not that I ever got much out of Mr. Wade, because, as Lucy said, " Dad was never a one for talking." I was too shy to try very hard, for he had a soft, growling voice, like an old dog that scents trouble, and once, when I locked him in the potting-shed as a joke, he had upended me without ceremony and given me the hardest and most richly-earned spanking I ever had. In any case I was overawed to see him in his own home, shorn of his old tweed cap he always wore to work, his hair brushed very stiff and shining into a quiff over his forehead.

Sometimes he would give hints of an almost feudal past, when he spoke of work at " th' great 'ouse " and of what "th' ole lord " had said, but where this was I never knew. Most often, the steak-and-kidney pie done, the plate scoured clean with bread, he would stare at me reflectively with his mild blue eyes, sometimes sucking his teeth, before giving me one great silent wink.

" Well, now, young shaver," he would say, and that was all, but from Mr. Wade it was an accolade almost, a hint that he acknowledged my presence.

But I knew more about his world than perhaps he thought. I absorbed it from Lucy on our walks. Old Mr. Beaver, who spent most of his day standing in a pond on the common, like a patient horse, clad in raincoat and waterproof top-boots, was at first a figure of fun to me, until Lucy identified him as " a very important gentleman—he works for all the big hospitals up in London and they think a lot of him." He collected horse-leeches, it seemed, which the hospitals put to some dark purpose, and " every night when he gets home he takes a big dose of medicine to keep off the shakes." Ever after, when Mr. Beaver squelched damply past us in the gloom, grunting a " 'Night t' yer," I was suitably impressed, remembering that.

No matter what failings village rumour laid at a man's door, Lucy and her father judged by older standards. What a man gave back to the soil which nourished him was their yardstick ; the rest was with God, inscrutable, beyond a mortal's power to probe. " I s'pose," as Lucy put it, " people just can't help being people."

So no matter that Mr. Pettishaw was cross and currish, made bitter and indrawn by the cleft palate which turned all his words into ugly gibberish—" he grows the best carnations 'tween 'ere and Dorking—Sir John made ever such a fuss until 'e went to work for him." Old Mr. Capper, who scythed our orchard, was a weird figure to childish eyes, with his white flowing beard like an Old Testament prophet and his ever-present stone beer jar, but " the farmers think the world of him. 'E's the only man left in these parts as can mow two acres a day." Memory quails to recall the grim eagle face of Mr. Pick, the common-keeper, with his brown bowler hat, corsetted gaiters and spiked stick

for impaling litter, but " 'e's very clever about wild flowers—
and knows all what the birds say to each other."

" 'Night t' yer, Lucy," would come their voices through the
dusk, " 'Night t' yer."

All these skills Lucy would recount to me as her kind rough
hands soaped me in the bath and guided the manœuvres of a pink
Celluloid duck. And I would go to sleep marvelling at all the
skills that I had never known were there to be mastered.

Well, they are all gone now, and since the war's end there
have been other footfalls in the lane at night: the brisk patter
of high heels coming from the big houses that have all become
insurance offices and banks, hurrying through the darkness to
catch the coach service back to London and civilisation.

But if the wind is right and I listen hard, I can hear other
sounds on the metalled road, the boots of those old men going
home, ringing through the dusk like horses' hoofs, and their
greeting comes gruff and kind, " 'Night t' yer, Lucy—'night
t' yer."

CHAPTER TWO

PRELUDE TO MEMORY

The joys of parents are secret, and so are their griefs and fears
FRANCIS BACON

IT IS strange to look back on that world now, far enough away in time yet whole centuries away in spirit. Yet my parents, when they made their home in this valley, had left another world behind them still. They were Londoners and when both of them first saw the light of day Victoria had twenty more years to reign.

In those days Santley Street, where my mother was born, and Azenby Square, where my father spent his youth, were typical of so many South London streets—solid yellow-brick terraces of Victorian comfort, their stone-flagged pavements lined with plane trees, each garden shut off from the street by green iron railings or privet hedges, each front door, with its polished brass handles, approached by a steep flight of hearth-stoned steps. Three-storied houses, they were, with areas, and basements to house the cockroaches and the wretched slaveys who toiled in them.

Yet even so the country was not far away. They were still hay-making at Camberwell in the nineties and as a little boy my father was often taken to pick wild flowers on Peckham Rye Common, half a mile away. Of course, the newer streets in both districts had their sprinkling of skilled craftsmen, head floor-walkers and Civil Service clerks and once out in the main high-ways—Brixton Hill, where my mother lived, or High Street, Camberwell—the whole clamorous workaday world crowded in on you. There were the markets with their naphtha flares, the brownstone " gin palaces " with the drunks in sodden collapse outside their doors, the ragged children, the horse-buses and the snarling whining roar of the trams.

Despite the nearness of this unwelcome world, there was no thought of moving into the real country, twelve miles away. My grandparents knew their place too well. The valley where I spent my youth was still living its life on the basis of the eighteen-fifties—small settlements of stone farm cottages, where the commercial giants who had unseated the old aristocracy now reigned as kings. Not until the ribbon development of twenties and the cross of rising taxes, when so many of these great houses became hospitals and finishing schools, was it fitting for a family like ours to make their home so far afield. In Queen Victoria's day a middle-class professional man's place was in the suburbs, close to London.

So this far the ways of life of the two families, the Hughesdons and the Colliers, ran parallel. Beyond that, all they stood for was poles apart.

There was a sadness in my mother's face which began in Santley Street. Almost everything about those years was over-hung by sadness. My mother's first memory of childhood was of sitting on the steps that led down to the basement kitchen, weeping bitterly because a fire in the range chimney was filling the room with black, terrifying smoke and being given some Osborne biscuits to still her tears. But these were not the only tears she shed at Santley Street. In repose you saw this shadow of sadness too often upon her face, and at times she was seized by a melancholy which led her to believe that the worst *must* happen and that everything which spelt hope was an illusion, a cheat imposed by life.

All the sisters—Eveline, my mother, who was the oldest, Muriel and Olivia—had the same melancholy. I cannot answer for the others, but with my mother I think it came from years of being told " No." Not that the cane or beating was a part of the household, though there were plenty of petty tyrannies like sitting three feet away from the meal table with arms folded and food a chilling mess if you ever, even by accident, set an elbow on the table. No, it was the dead dull routine that weighed down on them, my mother most of all, the stifling of every grain of curiosity and natural instinct, the emphasis on being respectable, whatever the cost.

Even the old yellowing photographs here on my desk show how beautiful my mother was. And there is no way to describe her but to say she had the face of a Madonna: the most serene smile I have ever seen, with cool grey eyes, and rich brown hair that was always naturally curly. I think of all three sisters she was the most talented, for at the Mary Datchelor School, Camberwell, which still exists, she carried off the prizes for French, English Composition, History and Nature Study as well as Art and Regular Attendance.

But I am not surprised at the " Regular Attendance." Life was so regulated in my grandmother's house as to make the ritual of *my* boyhood seem like a day at the fair.

Indeed that whole household was a twilight of the soul, with people as obsessed as any Oriental with the idea of losing face, and the real force behind it all was Grandma Hughesdon. Of course she was quite an old lady when I knew her, but the old photographs show that she had looked almost the same for years—the same strong jaw like a man's, the fierce grey eyes, the high imperious forehead. And every ounce of driving power she had was directed to one end—that neither she nor her husband nor her children, least of all her servants, should *ever*, in any way, besmirch the shining name of Hughesdon.

It led her to some strange passes, this obsession with face. She would not open her doors to anyone, except at infrequent intervals, in case it was said that she made free of her house " like a cheapjack proprietor." Callers might tiptoe through the portals, as they sometimes did, to present their cards, but when these were borne into the mahogany gloom of Grandma's drawing-room by a maid in a cap and ribboned apron, the answer, more often than not, would be " The mistress is not at home." Certainly nobody ever took " pot-luck " with Grandma.

Naturally there were exceptions. But very often they were

close friends who had called by arrangement, to report on the
way that a new servant carried herself. The wretched girl,
knowing nothing of his, would answer the door and show them
in, all unaware that the visitors—mostly ladies who saw things
the same way as Grandma—were just then reporting on everything the maid had said when she opened the door, how deeply
she curtsied, and how skilfully she had handled the silver salver
bearing the card. Yet with life going on like that, it was hard
indeed for her daughters to entertain their friends. My Aunt
Olivia met her husband, was courted by him and accepted his
proposal all within the four walls of Camberwell Public Library.

But I don't believe that Grandma could ever find much
real fault with her servants. They were all too well trained.
Every maid likely to answer the door went through the same
routine, and even those who passed the test had refresher courses.
Every so often Grandma and one of her daughters—usually my
mother—put on their cloaks and left the house. In stately
silence they walked a hundred yards up the road. In silence they
retraced their steps to the front door. To the maid who answered
it, Grandma would announce in ringing tones:

"I am Mrs. Brown. Is your mistress at home?"

Now, here was the testing time. Woe betide the girl who
seemed flustered, or who blurted out "I'll just see, m'm" and
made to hasten away. At once there would be an outraged snort
from Grandma: "Card, garl—card!" That was the cue for the
girl to pick herself up and say: "If you will give me your card,
madam, I will inquire within whether the mistress is at home."

What would have happened if the maid had come back and
said that the mistress wasn't at home, I don't know. But, of
course, she always was, so the charade ended with the maid
flinging open the drawing-room door and announcing stridently
to the empty room: "Mrs. Brown!"

I suppose the ideal maid had a manner which was assurance,
deference and self-possession all in one, for to one maid who
seemed too impersonal Grandma bayed out the immortal words:
"Make me welcome, garl—make me welcome!"

Apart from training them, Grandma's greatest concern was

for the morals of the girls who served her. None of them was allowed to wear veils on their hats, lest they became Above Themselves, and I believe they were not allowed to walk out at all, except to church on Sunday evenings. As soon as they got back they were mustered in the drawing-room to repeat the text of the sermon.

Not that Grandma's concern for her staff ever took her down to her own kitchen above once a year. This was at Christmas, to oversee the cook's mince pies, but as Grandma actually went down to the basement to view them, they were always known as " Mama's mince pies." And that was a solemn occasion. All the staff lined up on inspection, the pies browning away in the oven, and the cook hovering at uneasy attention close by. At the eleventh hour, the very picture of dignity, Grandma descended, looking, as she put it, when she wanted to emphasise true dignity, " neither to right nor to left." At the oven she uttered just one monosyllable : " Open ! " For an instant Grandma cast an eye upon the pies, then came the second command : " Shut ! " I believe the pies were always good and that ended Grandma's kitchen fatigue for another year.

It seems strange to me that my mother should have been rooted in such stony soil yet have nourished such a passion for beauty. Of course every Victorian young lady had her easel and colour-box ; that was a part of her life. And perhaps, too, it was a defence that she needed against the dead hand of the Hughesdon household. Yet with my mother all of it went deeper than a diversion for young ladies. She could sketch delicately and well—still-lifes, landscapes that had the cool mistiness of a Corot. She was a pianist with a delicate touch. Above all, she had the sensitive fine-wrought temperament of what she most wanted to be in life—an actress. That ambition had glowed within her, unfulfilled, ever since she was a little girl.

She was seventeen, she told me, before she dared to broach it. And, after all, there seemed a chance. It was the turn of the century. The old Queen had but three years to live. Henry Irving had been knighted, which seemed to set a seal of respectability on the whole profession.

Yet almost before she had stammered out her declaration of faith she knew it was no good. On every face she could read nothing but horror and disbelief.

" The garl," Grandma Hughesdon ground out, " must be sickening for something." Grandpa, an estate agent in a good way of business, was kindlier, yet it was still a struggle to convey the great social gulf that yawned between the professional man's family and the Green Room.

" My child," he said gently at last, " I don't believe you fully understand what you have said. Actors . . . actresses . . . these are people on a par with our servants."

And that was that. Once or twice my mother did try to resurrect the subject, but it was hopeless from the start. Grandpa Hughesdon could permit himself no more than a knitting of the brows—so much so that it was pointless even for Grandma to add : " Eveline ! Papa is displeased." That somehow was her special phrase when she felt my grandfather needed her moral support—though he rarely did.

So in the end it was not the footlights that claimed my mother. Eveline wanted adventure, she wanted independence—very well, Grandpa declared, she should have them. He was, he hoped, within reasonable limits a progressive man. There was perhaps no harm in a girl teaching or looking after other people's children—she might even work at the headquarters of the Savings Bank branch of the post office in West Kensington. When my mother chose this last alternative I think she was past caring. She stayed there for almost twelve years until she married my father in 1914 and every so often Grandma found it necessary to explain that " Eveline had no *need* to work—she's just full of new-fangled ideas."

I have a photograph of my mother, taken at that time, wearing a black silk ankle-length dress with white reveres, which speaks for itself. In all that office group of twenty girls she was the only one who could not summon a smile for the camera.

I suppose she had her share of pleasures but as she would tell me afterwards there was always that sense of oppression that seemed to stand between her and true happiness. Much later, when I had almost come of age, we stood one night in the garden and watched the glow of a late sun touch all the piled clouds above the valley with gold.

I remember how, watching them, I drew a deep breath and how my mother said quite simply " I used to watch the clouds a lot like that when I was a child—and think how, up there, *there* would be peace."

Yet never a hint of this marred the serenity of my childhood. My parents' lives, I supposed, had been as tranquil as my own, and in some ways this really was true of my father's childhood. But perhaps " tranquil " is hardly the word, as you will see.

Where the Hughesdon household at Santley Street was as dark as a funeral parlour—for it was one of Grandma's passions to economise on gas-light—the Collier households blazed with light and warmth and impassioned argument. I say "households" for as the rents were raised or perhaps went unpaid altogether— so the Colliers moved on undismayed from house to house, laying a trail of noise and unpaid bills and demolished idols across the back streets of South London. If the gas was cut off, as often happened, they would make do with candles. It did not stop them arguing.

If the Hughesdons had no greatness in their past the Colliers had it in plenty. Their lives were like Punchinello's, a see-saw of ups and downs, comedy seasoned with tragedy. They had served crowned heads and done exciting things, many of them outrageous. While a Warwickshire Collier had declared for Charles I, a Somerset Collier was one of the last men in England to be hanged for stealing sheep. Within my father's memory a Collier had acted with the great Macready and Dr. George Collier, who had consulting rooms in Spring Gardens, Whitehall, had been Court Physician to William IV. My great-aunt Amy Roselle (understandably she preferred this name on the billing to that of Eakins) had acted with the Kendals and the great Sothern before starring in *Our Boys* which still stands eleventh among the long runs of the London stage. She married Arthur Dacre, who leased the Haymarket Theatre, London and created that immortal rogue *Jim the Penman*. Subsequently he drowned her in a bath in Melbourne before cutting his throat over her lifeless body. The Colliers did nothing by halves.

When my father was a little boy the family was once again as down as it had ever been. Overshadowed all his life by Dr. George's greatness, his grandson, John, an unsuccessful accountant, had taken so kindly to the bottle that his family had pensioned him off to a farm near Penmaenmawr, Caernarvonshire. And with that, I think the Colliers' last willingness to compromise, to meet the world on its own terms, receded altogether. The family stood undivided, as tribal as any clan that declared for the Young Pretender, united by a hot and ready suspicion of anyone who was not a Collier.

All their feats were epic, of another century—violent in execution, yet as generous as if every man among them had a bottomless purse. They would argue with a man and punch his head as soon as look at him but if he needed money they would strip their pockets to the linings rather than let him starve. My Uncle Victor once thrashed a Covent Garden market-porter within an inch of his life for ill-treating a cat; he chose to do it beneath the windows of the Garrick Club yet he could never understand why they blackballed his application for membership. Another uncle walked to Newcastle and back, more than five hundred miles, to settle a £5 bet. They did these things, like all English eccentrics, not to attract attention but because they were unselfconscious and these were the things they most wanted to do just then. Liberty-loving sons of an old proud nation, they saw no need to justify themselves to the world.

A story they told about my Uncle Edmund will show you what I mean. He was sauntering along the street one day, minding his own business, when he saw, as he thought, one of the tribe bending to inspect a shop window. So at a run he went across the almost-deserted street and *thwack*! his walking stick came down with all his might on the seat of the other man's trousers. But for a moment then the words just left my uncle, for it was a total stranger writhing down there on the pavement.

34

When my uncle had helped him up and dusted him off, he could think of nothing in the world to say except, " I'm terribly sorry, sir—I thought you were my brother."

And the stranger too could think of nothing to say except the most heartfelt, " By Jove, I'm glad I'm not," that you could imagine. Always it was like that with the Colliers ; they understood perfectly what they were about and then the world had to break in and spoil it and write them down as " eccentrics."

Nourished on this rich broth, my father had absorbed from it both strength and weakness—his burning sense of justice, his irrepressible humour, his distrust of strangers. But there were things in which he was less a Collier—which was my good fortune, since he was the only one of the tribe, my mother said, whom she could ever have married. For once his father had disappeared from the scene, my Uncle William Henry became head of the family which by then incredibly numbered twenty-two, though not all survived the moment of birth. This made a deep impression on my father. He saw that times were lean and he became the only Collier of that generation to develop a taste for security. He wanted to marry and raise a family. He wanted a job and he was prepared to stick to it. He wanted to live in a house of his own without threat of dispossession.

His family accepted this as the individual brand of eccentricity to which every Collier was entitled. For among the twenty-two —fifteen brothers and seven sisters—only six had ever married.

But my father had seen what he thought were the danger signs. If the elder brothers were earning, the sisters weren't. Bread and potatoes appeared on the table in quantities to strike an Irish peasant dumb. On these, with a stew of the cheapest scrag-end, they had to make do, yet the talk was as heady as champagne—fierce, disputatious, timeless. You heard nothing, my father said, of " dirty old Kruger " or Jack the Ripper or the dashing Baden-Powell.

Instead, with a barrage of scorching oaths, they fought over the fundamentals of everything. It might be literature :

" Define Marlowe's contribution to the drama ! That's all I'm asking, you slant-eyed troglodyte—define it ! "

Or medicine :

" Lister ! Why, Lister was the sneering flunkey of medicine. Without Semmelweis, he'd have been nothing, I tell you, nothing ! "

Or even art :

" Since Michelangelo there's been no artist worth a bawbee. Constable was a scene-painter for side-shows. . . ."

Mind you, if you took most of it with a grain of salt, it was exciting. It gave you to think furiously. As a little boy my father had a lot of time for thinking. He was a weakly child, whose eyesight and digestion were poor, saved only by a hair's-breadth from succumbing to pneumonia. He could rarely attend school. Instead he was largely self-educated, as men did contrive to educate themselves in that era following the founding of the Mechanic's Institutes. His tutors were my Uncle William Henry and my Uncle Victor. Under their guidance he read voraciously the tiny pin-sized print of those days—Shakespeare, the Bible, Euclid, Plato, Plutarch's lives, every word that Dickens and his fellows ever wrote. He made plans to become a writer himself. But when Uncle William Henry—whose own quirk was a passion for security that put Shylock to shame—pressed the claims of the Civil Service, my father gave in. You could not support a wife and family by arguing like a Hyde Park orator. So for months he worked until his head swam but in the end he passed the stiffish Civil Service examination and joined the Standards Department of the Board of Trade in 1896.

Now this far he had my mother's approval. When they first met at a Wandsworth Common tennis-club in the spring of 1908 she was prepared to look kindly on a man with my father's strength of purpose. They had much in common. They liked queuing for the pit or the gallery to see *The Merry Widow* or Lewis Waller in *A White Man*. They liked cycling on the new free-wheel bicycles to picnic in the woods around Box Hill, my mother very fetching in a straw boater, white silk blouse with a brass-buttoned blazer jacket, full ankle-length skirt over hand-knitted black bloomers, my father in Norfolk jacket, outsize tweed cap and baggy plus-fours. They liked dancing and playing tennis and walking. It was natural that the friendship should ripen.

Then my father had to alter everything by falling in love. Being a Collier he fell in love as he danced or played tennis—absorbed, almost humourless, with the introvert's passionate desire to win through. My mother had nothing against falling in love but it was something to be achieved by degrees after a little parry and thrust. Other young men at the tennis-club, natty in their blazers and white flannels, meant less but said more. Their armoury included weapons like wit and neatly-turned compliments. Not so with my father.

In love he was like every Collier—as melancholy as Hamlet, withdrawn, given to vast sighs, his features contorted in a fixed and unrelenting scowl that spoke of passion. And at first my mother withdrew. None of the men she had met so far behaved like this. A dance should be a lightsome affair of Chinese lanterns and fruit-cup and lemon-water ices, with a small tasselled dance programme for a girl to inscribe, as fancy decreed, the names of intended partners.

Yet my father, finding that he did not feature large enough in one evening's programme, at once beat his breast and called on Heaven to witness that his affections were being trifled with. Convinced that all was over he next beat his head against a stone wall and to his own alarm drew blood. Strangely touched, my mother rendered what first aid she could.

The man was as mad as any of his brothers yet undeniably he cared.

By the first weeks of 1911 this single-minded courtship had produced results. For witness the letter which Grandpa Hughesdon wrote there and then on the office note-paper:

19th January, 1911

Dear Mr. Collier,

I have received your letter. I am pleased to give my consent to your engagement with Eveline and I hope you will both be very happy. With regard to means I should say you have quite sufficient to start with; I began on something like the figure you mention so that I can speak from experience, and as you have reasonable prospect of improvement there is no reason why you should not be comfortable.

We shall be pleased to see you in Streathbourne Road whenever you like to call and I hope it will not be long before you feel at home with us.

With kind regards,
Yours faithfully,
Edward Hughesdon

Three and a half years later, on 27th June, 1914, they were married at Holy Trinity Church, Upper Tooting, South London, with Uncle Victor as best man. The honeymoon was at the Lizard, in Cornwall. They had not been back a week before the lights, as a great man said, began going out all over Europe.

Yet they were lucky. The war produced no real upheaval in their lives. The poor health that had always dogged him kept my father from military service. Apart from now wearing a khaki reservist's brassard with a red crown to stave off the ladies who were free with white feathers he went daily to his office as before. My mother kept on with her job. But the ten years they passed in their cottage at Mitcham, Surrey, which was green countryside then, had only one end in view—the building of a house and the birth of a son.

And in the fullness of time both these things came to pass.

CHAPTER THREE

WHEN THE WORLD WAS YOUNG

---

*There is a feeling of Eternity in youth, which makes us amends
for everything*

WILLIAM HAZLITT

ALL THESE things I came to know little by little throughout
the years of my youth. But truly my parents were clever in that
until I was old enough to have it in perspective, never through
so much as a word did I suspect that their past lives had been
anything but happy.

Of course my father would laugh about how my mother had
" led him a dance " and my mother would recall the amazement
in first sitting down at a Collier meal-table—" everyone grabbing
with their fingers and talking nineteen to the dozen and insulting
one another—it was like going backstage at a circus." But
nothing of the sadness of *her* youth. Nothing of the grinding
poverty of *his*. And no hint at all that money sometimes could
be tight in our world too. I believe I had a security then which
few of us will ever know again.

And I know now that this was no accident but a security
which was planned as carefully as a new room or a new corner
of the garden.

At first I felt that security most in my mother's company.
Now that she was at last free of her family she could find outlet
for all the things she had wanted to do with her hands. Of course
she and other women like her were lucky. They had their Lucies
which made life very pleasant, so much time was there for learning

leathercraft and art needlework and transplanting begonias and stencilling—above all stencilling, for it was a ladylike accomplishment and it helped to pass the time. Why, I believe there was no corner of the house where my mother's stencils did not penetrate—stencilled wooden jewel-boxes, stencilled fire-screens, even stencils on the doors of cupboards, a pink spray of flowers perhaps entwined with vine leaves or a handkerchief-box adorned with a cloud of laburnum blossom.

But do not think that all my mother's time was taken up with such things. It was she after all who guided the first tentative probings of my mind and taught me to read by the time I was five—first Beatrix Potter, then Winnie the Pooh, and the now almost forgotten Olwen Bowen farmyard books, peopled by Hepzibah Hen and Gertie Grunter, to be followed soon by *Helen's Babies*. And listening to her soft almost husky voice with its attractive break these people came alive—they became more real almost than the people I knew, as so many favourite characters in books have been ever since.

And it was through my mother's eyes that I saw all this, for until I could snatch these delights for myself she was the sole interpreter and guide to the magic world that lay imprisoned inside the words. All the acting that had been denied came out there, of course, so that Eeyore had a different voice from Kanga—and if the authors had been remiss in failing to depict a scene, why then her drawing came in handy. It was my mother who would take crayons and good cartridge paper and delicately limn a scene as accurately as if the characters had been her creation.

All this I can remember, and my mother is so much a part of these memories because it was she who first showed me a wider view of the world beyond the bars of the cot. Yet it was a softened view, a secure view, to excite and quicken the curiosity, not to alarm, yet a view so vivid that it was hard to know where fantasy ended and truth began. Of course it was Beatrix Potter's world really, the small world of bright eyes peering from the grass; the Tailor of Gloucester and Peter Rabbit in old Mr. McGregor's cabbage patch.

To me, who had never stirred beyond a mile of our garden, it was as if the authors had been part of the scene and had woven the stories around it for me alone. The cabbage patch that Beatrix Potter drew was *our* cabbage patch, where old Mr. Wade wheezed over his spade with a robin in attendance. And weren't the six Corsican pines that stood on the heath half a mile away on a knoll carpeted with gorse, the same pine trees where Winnie the Pooh met his friends. I only knew the fantasy took hold of me so completely that for months I hauled my long-suffering teddy-bears to the spot every afternoon in the hope that we should surprise Piglet and Pooh at a tea-party.

I will never forget the day when I tried to explain something of this to Cousin Ethel, who was staying with us. A distant cousin of my mother's, she was, all good deeds for others, but tight lips and a tongue that dripped vinegar whenever she spoke, which was often.

" That's story-book stuff," she said, " and it sounds to me as if you were filling your head with rubbish. You don't seem to know the difference between what's true in life and what's in books."

Just then my mother came into the room and you should have seen her face as she heard.

" It seems to me," she said, and her words were like sharp stones, " that God gave a child its imagination to be used."

I could see Cousin Ethel was taken aback but she just sniffed and tossed her head.

" No good ever came out of day-dreaming," she said, with a tight little smirk, " of that I'm quite sure."

My mother just looked at her. She was as grave and lovely as ever but oh, the contempt in her face.

" If *we'd* listened more to *our* dreams," she said, " things might have been very different. A dream is something finer than us . . . all the things we wanted to be and couldn't. And a woman *will* dream, you know, Ethel, even if it's only at a kitchen-sink, and so will a man, even in a dusty office."

I should have guessed something about life in Santley Street then, but I didn't. It was years before I realised my mother's determination that the precious gift which had been denied to her should not in turn elude me.

I was too small to have the whole picture so clearly at four, of course, but life with my mother seemed to have been like that for years beforehand and went on much the same for years after. So I draw upon what I can remember from all the years and if the chronology is wrong here and there I know the feel is right. You don't always remember the way that *you* felt but you know how life felt, solid and warm and reassuring as the thick grey blanket that covered the cot.

I can remember that blanket and I can remember the sense of peace lying under it at night with the darkness made alive and friendly by the dancing shadows that the wax night-light, floating in its bowl of water, made on the bedroom wall. And I can remember—for again my mother was part of it—how I liked to awaken suddenly at ten, after four hours' sleep, and hear the stealthy rustle of garments as my parents undressed, their shadows black and gigantic against the wall.

Then I would murmur and cry out deliberately as if I was frightened because it would bring my mother near to me. And I would see the beauty of her face and stretch up my arms to feel the warmth of her body beneath the thin night-gown and smell the heady excitement of her perfume—wallflower perhaps, or attar of roses.

Those perfumes were always a part of the scene, for when my father wanted to give my mother a present he shopped, like most husbands, with a fine disregard of economics. For years my mother's dressing-table, with its hairbrushes and glove stiffeners and curling tongs, all backed with silver, was never free of the heavy cut-glass phials of Roger and Gallet perfume, like small whisky decanters, that my father had borne home in triumph.

Of course there were times when I was apart from my mother, especially when she was putting on her tea-party face to the world. Yet I know I felt a little surge of pride in knowing that she could do it and carry it off with the best of them.

Now if I had had brothers or sisters I suppose I would have

been packed off with them to the nursery at such times. Or if our house had been large enough to allow quarters for a full-time nursemaid I would have been away and taking my tea with her. But times were changing even then, so that while a few of the children from the big houses had full-blown nannies with starched caps trailing stiffly behind them and gruff voices like old Mr. Wade's, most of the houses round us were making do with their own Lucy, who was everything in one. So when my mother had a tea-party it meant that Lucy had to be parlour-maid in cap and apron, and there was I right in the thick of it.

I won't pretend that I liked it, because it meant a clean jersey and clean grey flannel shorts and scrubbed knees and what was worse, hair brushed hard and parted and smoothed down with a little water. And it meant not going out to play in the garden for fear of tumbling over and getting dirty, just sitting " out of the way " on a cretonne chair until the party began.

But I have always found a sort of fascination in watching other people closely when they weren't troubling about me, so there was some fun to be had there.

In the first place some of the ladies from what they said had either had their hair specially styled in London the day before or at least had it set at the local hairdresser's—all in honour of my mother's tea-party. Yet the strange thing to me was that none of them ever took off their hats from the moment they entered the house to the moment they left.

I can remember a few who did come without hats and who, in the height of summer, might just wear a cardigan and a printed dress ; they were the ones I liked the most and I suspect they were the ones my mother liked most, too, but usually they came on their own for a less formal cup of tea, for a professional man's wife had often to entertain according to status, like it or no.

From what I could gather the fact that they did not wear hats had something to do with their husbands being " in a poor way " —or as one of the less welcome tea-time visitors once put it, " not quite out of the hanky drawer."

But the regulars would sit there always rather on the edges of their chairs, I thought, and using their hands a great deal as they talked—with those close-fitting cloche hats of felt or velvet quite obscuring their shingled curls and probably wearing long three-strand necklaces of amber beads and neat two-piece tailor-mades, with suède gloves and marten stoles. And the mark of a lady in those days was that while she would retire upstairs on arrival to remove her furs, she removed only the glove of her right hand in order to eat her tea.

From the way the food was spread about, you would have thought that my mother was set to feed a troop of Boy Scouts. There was the four-tier brass cake-stand, shiny and resplendent, laid out with every kind of cake you could think of—the sponge cake layered with jam and cream and dusted with sugar, the walnut cake all studded with crisp sweet kernels, and perhaps an iced chocolate cake with a cream filling. All of them, uncut mark you, for it wasn't done to offer a cake which lacked a slice. But these were just to set the final edge on the feast after you had worked a way through the cut bread and butter with one of three kinds of jam, the cucumber sandwiches (cucumber seemed to be " correct," while tomato was not), the scones, the chocolate biscuits, the bourbon biscuits, and the bridge rolls with anchovy paste. To crown it all there would be the best silver tea-service and the Minton tea-set, with every cake reposing on its own special crocheted doily. And everyone had their own silver tea-knife and their own small damask napkin, never paper ones because, as my mother said, " it isn't a picnic in the garden."

Yet after all that it seemed to me that a plate of bread and butter would have done as well. I was for ever being prodded to spring up and offer plates of cake to ladies who didn't want them, who could summon up no more appetite than to nibble at a cucumber sandwich or to drink a cup of tea with lemon floating in it—" I really shouldn't, you know, I'm on this no-starch—no-sugar diet for a few days." And there was only one exception to that rule—by some subtle hint my mother was supposed to make it plain which cake was " home-made " and which was " bought." Once that was established for sure, there was reason enough to depart from the diet—" Oh, well, of course, if you *made* it . . ."

They partook lavishly of that; the other cakes went back to the kitchen uncut and Lucy and I made short work of them in the days that followed.

In the end, I believe, there was no more reason for those cakes being there than there was in polishing the shoes every morning, for lighting a fire in the dining-room as well as the drawing-room whenever visitors were expected. I suppose it was as necessary to show that you had the cake as to show that you had the coal.

What the visitors wanted to do above all was to talk. Sometimes there might be two hours of talk while I could only nibble at sandwiches to show good manners, scrubbed and mutinous in the background, in receipt of no more than a wan and distant smile from any guest who happened to intercept my scowl. And how they talked! They talked about recipes for cauliflower *au gratin* and bramble jam, about matinées followed by tea at Gunters or Fullers—" We'd love to do an evening show sometimes but the children are *such* a tie "—and about Owen Nares, Gerald du Maurier and Leslie Banks, who seemed to be the principal attractions the matinées had to offer.

They talked about Warwick Deeping's new best seller and about the latest issues of *Nash's* and *The Windsor Magazine* and about holidays at Cromer and Torquay and Frinton-on-Sea. (Very few families, even those that could afford it, ever seemed to go abroad.) Next month, I knew too well, they would discuss these things all over again.

Sometimes, to my great relief, it would end in a few rubbers of bridge, which meant a fresh pack of cards and little scoring pads and new freshly-sharpened pencils and meant, too, that I could slip gratefully away to Lucy in the kitchen. But whether that happened or not, always, when tea was over, someone would produce a case and rather diffidently ask the others in turn " Er—do you . . . ? " And quite a few were apt to colour and answer, " Well—er—I must say I *do* rather like one after tea."

Of course, we all knew that the girls my father called " flappers " smoked but women of my mother's generation were only really toying with the habit at the close of the nineteen-twenties. And some were worldly wise enough to admit yes, *they* rather enjoyed just the *occasional* one, too. So when the daring ones had lit their cigarettes they would puff away awkwardly with a sense of vice shared behind closed doors, thinking themselves most sophisticated.

Is it any wonder that I had such a sense of security? When life goes on like that, week in, week out, unchanging and seemingly unchangeable, then indeed childhood is a happy time.

And my father, too, though I saw less of him then, worked as hard to see that it was not destroyed.

I can see that now in a thousand ways that I never understood. Like the time—though this came later—when I ran home from school full of the wonderful present that Santa Claus had brought to Davy Butcher who was a friend of mine.

" A wonderful model of the Blue Train, he says, and if it's all right please can I go to tea and play with it? It has little pink lamps like they have in Pullmans and a conductor and passengers and it whistles through tunnels . . ."

And my father, his eyes twinkling through his spectacles, was trying to stem the tide the best he could : " Hold on, old chap! How did Santa Claus get all this down the chimney? "

" Don't know. But he did—Davy says so. And it's got little pink lamps . . ."

" And you'd like Santa Claus to bring you one like it, is that it? "

" Well . . ."

Head hung now and shuffling a bit. It was wrong, I knew, to ask grown-ups to intercede with Santa Claus. It was like trying to make a bargain with God when you knelt by the bedside to say your prayers.

" Well, I'll tell you my suggestion, old chap. I'd write it down for Santa Claus and see what he does. But I wouldn't hold out too much hope, because he takes the size of houses into account and I doubt if ours is big enough to have a train like that. But we'll see what happens . . ."

And I remember the time when my father came home from the office looking tired one night—and this must have been later, too, because I know I was sitting up but reading a book. They were talking and my mother said: " I see that the Remingtons are having their house done up. Boards outside the gate and everything."

Both of them had a look at me then, though they didn't think I knew it. Then my father said, " Do you think it's about time we did ? "

And looking back I can see that it was, for the paper was already peeling in places and the plaster was beginning to crack.

But my mother said, " Oh, I don't know——"

" You can if you like, dear, you've only to say the word——"

Funny how I got the impression that it was for my benefit they were talking and not for their own at all.

Silence for a little, while my father wiped his spectacles and gazed at the mantle, then my mother said, " Well, I don't know. It's such a bother, you know, having workmen in and getting all the dust-sheets out and everything. I think if it's all the same to you I'd rather wait until next year——"

So often things had had to wait until next year but in a way there was security in that too : everything as serene and peaceful as a long summer's day. It must have been about that same time that I came into the room one day and caught just the tail-end of a remark from my father—" pretty heavily in the red."

Now I guessed this to be slang but slang has always fascinated me so I waited until the time was ripe then asked my father what it meant.

" In the red ? Well, it means overdrawn at the bank, you know. It means you owe them money that you might find difficult to pay back."

" Is that a bad thing ? "

" Sometimes it is. Sometimes it means you're spending more than you can afford. And that *is* a bad thing. It means that whatever other people may think, you're hard up."

" Are *we* in the red then ? Are *we* hard up ? "

My father laughed. " Everybody *says* they're hard up, old son. What do you think ? "

I thought of the wonderful blaze of colour that the garden was

just then and of my own bedroom with the teddy-bears ranged
solemnly on the window-sill and of Lucy and old Mr. Wade,
who were always there, no matter what, and of the fat good
smells that never failed to come from the kitchen every meal-
time—a glorious swooning mixture of steak-and-kidney pudding
and treacle tart and Irish stew and blackberry pie——No, these
things were too solid and reassuring to be a lie. I lived here
so I knew.

We were not in the red. We were not hard up. Life was still
secure.

.   .   .

That was thirty years ago. The other day, rummaging in a
cupboard for a note-book I had lost, I found it, or so I thought
and was swiftly turning the pages.

But what was this? " Overdraft £150 "—— " Overdraft
£250 "—— " Overdraft £300 "—— I had not written this.

It was an old note-book of my father's, almost identical in
binding and shape to the kind I use myself. It must have lain
there for years. I looked at the dates then : 1929—1930—1931.
And I remembered my father's words : What do you think ?

Well, had I really thought at all ? I had gone on selfishly,
accepting, never thinking so long as I was comfortable. But my
father and my mother had thought.

They had thought correctly that I would forget all about the
Blue Train, given time ; they had thought that at a boy's school
the will of Santa Claus is immutable and so saved my face.
They had thought what to say every time the house needed
decorating or when my mother needed a new dress or when a
strange and enticing toy appeared in our local shop.

I have thought too since then but no words will come. And
how to beg forgiveness from those who have gone to dust these
long years ?

CHAPTER FOUR

OTHER THINGS THAN LESSONS

Somebody has said, that a king may make a nobleman, but he cannot make a gentleman

EDMUND BURKE

ALL THIS morning the house has been so quiet you might have heard a mouse move, and here I have sat, in tune with its stillness, reshaping my life in thought. Not that a mouse or any creeping thing would find sanctuary here now, for every penny I have earned these years has gone to making bricks dry and damp-proof, every room snug and warm and to armouring old wood and crevices against rain and wind.

Only the swallows still return to the eaves each spring, swooping darts of indigo from the hot lands beyond the seas, and they are welcome always.

Perhaps it is silly to feel like this about a little house, one that holds no memory of palanquins or priests' hiding-holes or red rose warring with white. But a house is a home when all is said and done and there is a secret indestructible framework of memories supporting its walls which no stranger ever sees but which are as firm as iron bars.

I will never forget the surprise I had the day I learned it would one day be mine. For I was no more than five years old at the time.

I was trotting round the garden with my father, and he, as usual, had his pipe going well but every now and then he would pause on the Cumberland stone path and cock his head critically.

49

First the gutters were choking up with autumn leaves; we must have a man up to clear them at once or the drain pipes would get blocked. And the trellis-work that was joined to the house where the rambler roses twined—that was a disgrace. Old Mr. Wade must get busy on that with some creosote.

"Dad," I asked patiently, "is the house all you ever think about?" Straight to the point, you see, because I wanted to have done with this domestic detail and talk about cowboys.

My father grinned at first, then after a bit he was serious again. "Well," he said, "it's mostly because of you, after all."

Now it was my turn to be surprised, for the thought had never even crossed my mind. "*Me?*"

"You. Do you know what a son and heir is."

"Yes. There's the sun up there—and air's what we're breathing."

My father swallowed, all much-needed patience. "Now—just try and understand. You're my son—and you're my heir, too. That means that one day all this will be yours. The house—the garden—everything."

"*All* of it? Even the trees?"

I don't know why I should have thought the trees might not be part of the bargain. But it was just too big to grasp all at once, like being given the glossiest, most powerful rocking-horse in the world when it wasn't even your birthday.

But my father agreed, yes, even the trees, although he added, "Except you know that you never really own trees or flowers—you hold them in trust for God." A lot of fathers might have felt self-conscious, saying that to their sons, but my father really believed it and he was enough of a Collier not to mind saying what he thought.

That night, when I was sitting up in bed sipping hot milk and moving mountains to avoid the skin on top, my father came as he always did to say good night. And the subject came up again.

"You remember what I said to-day about the house? About it being yours one day?"

"Yes, Dad." But I was sleepy and most of the surprise

had gone now because it all seemed too far away. I wasn't even sure that I wanted a house—a galleon flying the skull and cross-bones might be more fun——

"Well, I meant it. I don't know—someday it might help to know that. It's not very much but it's all I can give you."

This had all my attention. I never wanted a lot, but for a second I had the terrifying notion that in return for this far-off gift of a house I was to forfeit comics, teddy-bears, lead soldiers, toy animals for my farmyard for ever and ever. And suddenly I was bolt upright in bed trying every way I knew to persuade my father to take his gift back again. I didn't really deserve it—I wouldn't know what to do with it——

"Now, now, old son," said my father soothingly, "don't get excited. Only when you grow up there's something you'll want to be—and whatever it is I won't stand in your way. But probably there'll be nothing I can do like introducing you to people who could help you unless it's the Civil Service you want."

Suddenly he cleared his throat and I was wide awake and listening with an understanding beyond the age of five because I knew he was finding this hard. He fiddled about with his hands, straightening a picture, looking for something to do.

"Anything you want to do," he said, "you'll mostly have to do yourself. It will all be up to you. Support—that's all I can give you. And I shan't leave a lot of money. But there will be the house."

The light went out. "Good night then," he said from near the door, "and sleep tight, old son. God bless you."

So he left me quiet in the darkness, with sleep walking on tiptoe towards me, thinking of a future I could not picture with destiny already on the pillow beside me.

.   .   .

If you think this knowledge shaped me overnight into a different boy, you are much mistaken. The thought that the house might one day be mine didn't stop me from leaving a rogue's gallery of fingerprints all the way down the wall by the staircase or from bringing a slather of mud to the good Axminster in the hall.

But what I learned in those years was still a preparation for what came after, for if the man is to inherit a kingdom of peace and beauty, however small, the boy must first learn the things that will help him not to disgrace his heritage.

"Do as you would be done by" was what my father tried to impress on me above all, and if I heard him quote it once in my boyhood I heard it a hundred times. A good motto if you can live up to it, too, for there are many sly actions we would think twice about doing if we took the time to analyse how we would feel in the other man's shoes.

But my father was one who took that time and trouble, both at home and away, in great things and in small. If the sun looked like pitting all his strength against one part of the garden, my father would never leave for the office before seeing that old Mr. Wade's job for the day would keep him in the shade, beyond risk of heat-stroke. And at midday, along with Mr. Wade's good lunch, there would be a pint of cold dark beer with a creamy head on top, for we were a long way from an alehouse and my father would not hear of Mr. Wade going without his beer.

It was just the same at his office, for though there were personnel officers in plenty and the messengers had no real right to bother the head of the department with their troubles, it was to my father they always came if a favourite son was running a bit wild or a neighbour was out to cause trouble. And my father would listen gravely, cool blue clouds arising from his pipe, offering what advice he could even when he was already late to take the chair at some big conference or other.

Of course one of the reasons for my father's interest was that most of the messengers were ex-servicemen. That meant more to everyone than it does now, yet to my father, who was not even in the war, it meant more than to any man I ever knew.

"They did their bit," he used to say, which was the phrase of the time, but I know he pictured how it would have been to be separated from my mother in those years, perhaps to come back lamed or blind, with the thunder of the shells in his eardrums for eternity. So he listened to the messengers' problems by the hour and if a little shuffling band of street musicians with their cornets and their trap drums and their " Ex-Servicemen " placard loomed out of the London fog my father would be fumbling at once for his silver, even if it left him short for the rest of the day.

One of the very first books my father ever bought me was a fine edition of *Æsop's Fables*, with colour plates interleaved, and though he knew that I would enjoy them he had a deeper object in view. The dog snarling from the manger, the mouse nibbling at the lion's cords, the silly milkmaid with her pail—all these were fables that I grew to love, which must needs be read to me time and again.

Yet each one of them was really recounting in new guise the strong and simple truth that was my father's creed : that the sum of all the world's lessons is the lesson of humility. This was the truth that was graven on his heart and he cared more than anything that I should learn it too.

I won't say that some aspects of this lesson weren't painful at the time. The meaning of words, for instance, and what goes to make a gentleman.

Until I was five the only person I had ever heard talk of ladies and gentlemen was Lucy. When Lucy talked about " a lady " she meant someone who didn't soil her hands with housework, while a gentleman wore fine clothes with a buttonhole and perhaps had his own car. So it was natural I should think the same.

That was until Lucy had to take a few weeks off to nurse her mother and someone recommended Lily to take her place.

Now Lily had not been with us three days before it was plain she would not last three weeks. My mother would see to that. She was a big slummocking girl with cropped hair and braying laugh, as awkward around the house as a young bullock and about as useful. If she and her broom encountered dust of a morning then the place for it was under the drawing-room carpet, double quick. Afternoon walks with Lily meant just a quick turn down to the farm, to loiter bored in the rickyard while she and young Harold, the cowman, snorted over private jokes and punched each other in the ribs. Bidden by my mother to take what she fancied for lunch Lily ate, without blinking, half a rabbit pie and a third of a Dundee cake. I heard a lot from my mother on the subject of Lily.

I wasn't sorry to hear she was going and one evening when my mother was late home I decided I was going to have no nonsense from her myself. My father was in the drawing-room sipping his sherry behind closed doors and I was in the kitchen, resisting Lily's efforts to send me to bed.

" Great fat lump," I shouted, past all patience, " I won't go —not till I'm ready."

" You young 'ound," said Lily deeply hurt, " I'll tell yer dad on yer."

To do her justice she wouldn't have done ; I knew her good nature too well and already I was feeling a twinge of shame at what I had said. But to-night there was to be a reckoning. Only a second later I heard my father call.

I felt all my courage drain out through my boots just then for I had never heard him so stern.

Through to the drawing-room I went, and at the sight of him my stomach quivered as if a live bird was in it, for his eyes were as cold as the winter sea behind his spectacles and his lips were tight with contempt.

" Stand there," he said, " stand still where I can look at you."

" Yes, Dad," I said, very eager to please all of a sudden.

He interlaced his fingers, so like a judge that it seemed as if it was the black cap for me then and there.

" Is there any need," he asked, " for Lily to come and tell me what you called her ? Or are you man enough to tell me yourself ? "

I bit my lip, for I knew that if I sought refuge in tears now he would despise me. " Repeat it then," he said, in a more ordinary voice. " See how it sounds to you now."

So I repeated it, wishing for a great merciful hole to appear in the drawing-room carpet and swallow me up. But there was so long a silence after that I couldn't tell which way the wind was going to blow.

" Now then," my father said at last, " would I say a thing like that to Lily ? Can you imagine it ? "

" No, Dad."

" Well—why not, do you think ? Try and think—why not ? "

The sternness had died from his voice now, as if the fire of anger had burned low, yet left a chill of disappointment, which was worse. But I couldn't put what I wanted to say into words.

" Look here," my father said, " if I spoke like that to Lily, would she be able to answer me back the same way ? If she wanted to keep her job, I mean ? "

I shook my head because I knew that was true.

" So if I did, it should be taking advantage of her, shouldn't I ? And a gentleman doesn't do that. You see, a gentleman doesn't take advantage of anyone, especially anyone who depends on him. And do you know another thing a gentleman doesn't do ? He never speaks like that to a lady, no matter how he's feeling."

" But," I said feebly, " it was Lily," thinking of fine ladies who did no housework.

My father was looking at me gently now. He got up and put his two hands on my shoulders.

" Now, look, my son," he said, " get this into your head—because if you don't, nothing you ever do in life will be worth anything.

" There are gentlemen living in castles and there are gentlemen delivering milk. You aren't born a gentleman, whatever they say. You prove yourself one. And one of the ways you prove yourself one is by never taking advantage of anyone weaker. Do you understand ? "

" Yes, Dad," I said.

Now his smile was kind indeed. " There aren't ladies and maids, you know," he said, " only ladies. And a gentleman treats every one the same, with courtesy and consideration, not cruelly or with meanness. Your mother and all women. Will you remember that ? "

" Yes, Dad," I said again, and now I began to see why he had always raised his hat to Lucy if we had met her in the lanes.

" Good boy," he said, " then go and tell Lily you're sorry. And if I never have to say this to you again, I'll be proud enough."

.   .   .

Of course my father had his share of faults, he would have been less than human otherwise, but they were not such as gave my mother real cause for worry. But he enjoyed being master in his own house in the absolute way that men were still masters twenty years after the death of King Edward. With good servants to do their bidding and no call to lend a hand with household chores, it was easy for them to be so. I believe my father was secretly proud of being, as he said, " constitutionally incapable of boiling a kettle " and I am sure he never so much as poached an egg in his life.

So if my mother was ever ill, which mercifully was not often, Lucy needed to be at our house from sunrise to last thing at night to keep things going smoothly. Not that she needed to cook much for my father then, or rather not at the time I am thinking of now, the time when my mother had a bad 'flu cold.

The doctor assured us it was no more than that and what my mother needed above all was rest—good restful sleep. But my father shook his head, fearing the worst. He loved my mother deeply and he began to worry.

He worried so much that soon he could not eat at all. A sense of waiting for something awful to happen crept through the house. The 'flu cold became by degrees something so awful that you dared not speak the word aloud. But my father's face confirmed your worst suspicions.

What was worse, my father would not go to work. He took time off from the office and stayed at home, walking on tiptoe about the house and whispering. He infected everyone else with this until even the doctor lost some of his bounce and began whispering and walking on tiptoe too.

You cannot imagine the effect of this on my mother's nerves. All the hours she might have been enjoying good restful sleep she found herself staying awake, trying to hear my father as he tiptoed past the bedroom door. She listened for him through the closed door, nerves tight-strung, like a lone housewife keeping track of a burglar prowling on her porch. A few days of this had her in worse shape than ever. There was nothing for it but to get well again as quickly as possible.

The way my father took his time was another thing that made its impact on my mother. Not that she objected to the leisurely way he shaved or breakfasted but she liked to organise her day and get down to things and sometimes my father's plan for living life to the full got in the way. Not that he ever realised it for then he would have made valiant efforts to change and have got in my mother's way more than ever.

Take his Sunday bath now, a very different thing from his brief daily baths. Looking back I remember that three hours of a Sunday morning were taken up by my father's bath, with Lucy coming in especially after church to stoke as hard at the boiler as if our house was a ship sailing on that afternoon's tide. All that time the water had to be kept piping, for my father liked three changes of hot water before he felt himself spruce enough to face the Sabbath day. On his back in that bath he wallowed, still smoking his pipe, the steam misting his spectacles and streaming down the tiled walls. And all the while he sang.

Sometimes he would sing a hymn or an aria or two but mostly it was one song over and over again, Adela Florence Nicolson's "Pale Hands I Loved." Every week, for almost three hours, the house was like a sound-box, shaking with it, and what was worse my father could not sing. He was as off-key as any man has a right to be, yet I think the music sounded good to him in the way that every man is a Caruso in the solitude of his bathroom :

> *Pale hands I loved beside the Shalimar—ah*
> *Where are you now ? Who lies beneath your spell ?*

It was a blessed relief when weekdays came again because

now my father's bathing was briefer. The shaving and the breakfasting and the dressing all took too much time for my father to mourn those " pale hands, pink tipped " which he would rather, he told the world, have felt round his throat " crushing out life " than waving him farewell.

In the matter of change my father was a man to put his foot down. Uncompromisingly he resisted change—any kind of change—as if the secret of life was living it to a pattern like a fugue of Bach's, and one note altered in the music made all things false. There was a stair-rod we had which was broken in the early days of the house and broken it stayed for fifteen long years; my father had an aversion to seeing it mended because in some indefinable way it recalled the, happy, trivial past and later my mother had no heart to trouble about it. And yet when the stair-rod went away, along with so much else that I had to scrap, I felt stupidly disloyal because of it.

I felt much the same way over the plumbing, though my mother had strong feelings on that all the years we lived here. Our water-pipes had been laid, unlagged, close to the outside walls of the house and there was a network of them in the roof unprotected from bitter weather. The pipes should have been lagged and the roof boarded in but when the builder asked if this was to be done my father said No.

He had no head for the mysteries of construction and I think he was too proud to ask the builder why lagging was necessary. But came the first brisk snapping winter, when frost seized the ground and the earth was as hard as a barn door, and he knew. All the pipes, even the outside wastes, became no more than solid ice clamped round by lead. You had to climb a ladder outside the back door and sluice kettles of boiling water down the pipes to get water to stir from a wash-basin.

When the thaw came the pipes began to burst. They burst in places where the plumber had not even suspected there *were* pipes. The landing and the hall and every upstairs room were spread with buckets and pie-dishes and pudding-basins set to catch that steady insidious drip-dripping that came from the dark spreading stains across the ceiling. Now clearly was the time to have the pipes lagged and the roof boarded in. But my father hesitated.

" Perhaps one day," he said, adding as always when nothing on earth was going to hurry him, " I shall have to think about it."

Twenty years later he was still thinking about it and my mother was thinking about it and talking about it quite a lot, too. But I think she knew from the beginning it was hopeless. It would have involved change, a change that my father wouldn't have had before his eyes, but change just the same. My mother loved my father so she put up with it, which I think is more than most wives would to-day.

She put up with my father's tactics on bills, too, though at times I think her patience came close to breaking point. And that indeed was a comical business looking back on it, for while my father was quite able to pay such bills as came his way he had a strange reluctance to paying any of them, or so it seemed, until a writ was almost pending.

" I believe in being careful," he would say, and it never failed to drive my mother wild.

" Careful ? " she said, her voice two tones higher. " If the bill's in, I suppose it's got to be paid sometime ? What do you mean, careful ? "

" Well," said my father reluctantly, " I don't believe in taking risks." As if the bill were open to negotiation like a peace treaty, you see, and a waiting game at the conference table might prove it all to be a mistake.

" Now look, Charles," my mother would say when a week or two had gone, " this bill's been gathering dust for almost a month. Are you going to do something about it or not ? "

And my father would say yes, without fail, although most likely he would forget to take the bill to the office with him unless my mother snatched it up and pressed it on him before he left. You might ask why she didn't prise a cheque out of him and send if off herself but somehow in those days a man clung jealously to that male right of settling the bills.

But it was not long before my mother realised that this system had broken down. At first she felt her duty done if she asked my father that night whether he had made out a cheque for the gas or whatever it might be. My father would say yes, for he always told her the truth. He would not add, because he had forgotten, that he had sealed the cheque in an envelope along with the bill, and put it back in his breast pocket.

All would be peace for a time until the gas company's final notice came in with the porridge one fine morning, red-lettered and threatening. Then my mother's indignation knew no bounds. She called on my father to turn out his pockets and there, nestling inside his wallet, was the unposted envelope.

"Really, Charles," she said, her fingers making a small tattoo on the breakfast table, "after all I've said—look, give it to me and I'll post it myself this morning. Do you want us to be cut off?"

But sometimes it was not so simple. It might be the final notice itself which my father bore off to the office insisting that he, the man of the house, must settle all bills personally. If that happened a man would arrive next week from the water-board or the gas company to cut us off that minute. Once he arrived during one of my mother's tea-parties. She settled the bill on the spot with murder in her heart.

When my father came home that night she resorted to a good woman's last refuge. She burst into tears. Thus she sought to bring home to my father the distress he had caused her, but it worked too well.

My father was cut to the quick. He believed sincerely that an Englishman must be scrupulous about settling his debts but it was the same as with lagging the water-pipes; he wanted time to think about them. Next morning, seeing the red-lettered final notice still staring accusingly from the dining-room sideboard, he was seized by remorse.

He took the bill straight off to the office, ignoring the stamped receipt, and paid it all over again.

This drove the gas company to distraction. It did not suit them to be paid twice because it put their books out of order, but at the same time they were loath to send the money back.

They wrote to explain this to my father and explained that they would credit our account in the next quarter accordingly.

So for the time being we were straight with the gas company but probably not with the other companies for there were still bills for the rates, the telephone and the electricity to vanish into my father's wallet. We reached a climax of sorts one morning when my father was at the office, turning out his wallet, and came across a small sheaf of them.

This time the remorse was like a knife in him, so stabbing-sharp that he hardly paused to think what he was about. Making out a cheque to the electricity board he posted it in an envelope addressed to the water-board, along with the bill the telephone manager had sent. It took them weeks to sort that out, and every now and then my father sent a letter to them all apologising, which had them in a worse tangle than ever.

My mother was on the brink of tears at the moment when she realised what he had done but then I suppose the richness of it was too much for her and she laughed to make the pictures fall down.

She must have realised there was no changing my father but if she could have lived her life over I think she would have had it the same, bills and all.

CHAPTER FIVE

AN AFFAIR OF THE HEART

One and one make two, two and two make four,
this was to me a childish sing-song
CONFESSIONS OF ST. AUGUSTINE

OF COURSE this unclouded happiness had to end for me some time, and end it did. One morning when I was five years old I had such a shock that for a moment the bottom seemed to drop out of my world.

The sun was shining brightly and I was all dressed up in clean jersey and shorts, but where were we setting off to walk to, so early on a morning in late spring?

"School," said my mother, trying to outdo the sun in the brightness of her smile. "You're a big boy now."

Well! If I had ever thought of school it was as something a very long way off, like getting married or going into business. I was so stunned that I could offer no protest for all the half mile of walk—across the valley, past the parade of shops and the railway station and all the way up the opposite hill.

And there it was, a rambling red-roofed private house, rough-cast walls overgrown with feathery green creeper, with acres of lawns and tennis courts and playing fields to set it off and a carriage sweep carpeted with bright yellow gravel. To crown it all, a big wooden notice-board on stilts with neat gilt lettering: " St. Hilda's School for Young Ladies and Gentlemen. Proprietress, Mrs. Helen Ogilvie."

So before I could even say " I want to go home " my mother

had led me through a shaded hall cool with tall vases of narcissi and smelling of wax polish and up the stairs to the headmistress's study. And then and there, for the first time in my life, I knew real fear.

Not because this idea of school was alien to me, for there were other mistresses I came to like well enough. But a child can sense cruelty as an animal can and be as ready to cringe from it or to fight back if it thinks it stands a chance. And I could smell out the cruelty of Mrs. Helen Ogilvie even then, though soon I was to have positive proof of it. Even as she said, " Come here, Dickie. Are you an obedient child ? " I was ice-cold and braced with dislike.

Dislike of the deep mannish voice and of the velvet cloche hat set as squarely as a helmet on her head ; dislike of the ample bosom strung with pearls, of the thick lips pursed above the bulldog jaw, of the eyes that stared unwinkingly through almost opaque horn-rimmed spectacles. They were brown eyes, quite expressionless even when she was angry, except that then tiny yellow flecks seemed to dance in them.

Now it was right enough that I should be cut down to size and within twenty minutes of my mother's leaving me but there were ways of doing that, after all.

I had not known, you see, that this golden morning was to be devoted to school, so in setting out I had armed myself as usual with a toy six-shooter. A fine nickel-plated affair, it was, the very pattern of those the sheriffs carried in coloured comics like *Crackers* and *Chums*.

By the time I had freed myself from Mrs. Ogilvie it was the " tuck break " but my mother had not known this. She had left me no money. Aggrieved, I wandered into the playground and espied a group of children playing a game by themselves at the far end.

They had their backs to me but I did not intend to be ignored if I could help it. Whipping out my six-shooter I piped out, " Stick 'em up ! "

Without a word of warning the world fell in on me.

As one, they turned. As one, they yelled—a tidal wave of

sound telling me in no uncertain terms that here I had bitten off more than I could ever chew. And as they raced at me, howling like Maoris on the warpath, I fled, and now others joined the pursuit until within seconds there were half a hundred frenzied five-year-olds at my heels.

In a moment I had lost my balance and gone headlong, with that hated yellow gravel searing my bare knees, scared stiff at the tornado I had unleashed, with the roar of their triumph drowning out my noisy sobs.

Then they were silent and I looked up through a mist of tears and there was Mrs. Ogilvie, just standing and watching.

" Oh, dear," she said not moving, her deep voice as soft as beside a sick-bed, " we have a little hooligan amongst us." And she smiled.

A soft smile it was, a smile that just twisted her mouth a little and then it was as if it had never been and her voice was cutting like a whip : " Stand up, you little beast—stand up and explain yourself."

But I was so shaken by tears that I could not, so for the first time but not the last I felt her hands upon me : cold hands that dug deep into the flesh of my neck and hauled me on to my feet. And her grip never once relaxed as if it was in sympathy with her voice and liked to pinch and hurt while she propped me there to wound me with words that I only half understood : "— wretched child—brandishing offensive weapons—inciting innocent children to riot——"

Yet I felt that chill of fear again, there in the sunlight, for it was no sharp spurt of anger such as my parents would summon up. It was a voice soft, deep and excited that was relishing my plight all the while like a good dinner. And I knew it would be war between us until the end.

I spent the rest of that tuck break in disgrace, standing in a corner, hands clasped behind my back, facing the wall. The six-shooter had already been confiscated ; I never saw it again. It was hardly a good beginning.

.   .   .

I never hated anything in life so much as those three years at St. Hilda's. And that is not surprising. Already I was learning other things than the subjects listed on the end-of-term reports still filed away in my father's old desk : Scripture, Recitation, Reading, Painting, Nature, Class Singing——

I was learning that a crowd can be a lonely place and that is a hard lesson to learn at the age of five.

Of course the whole system of schooling that we had then was to blame in some ways. Whatever may be said about education now, there are fewer girls' day schools like St. Hilda's with mixed kindergartens attached but there were hundreds in the years between the wars, when there were more girls than boys, and we had to make the best of them.

But it was hard to find friends in such a place for of a hundred or so pupils who gathered in the main classroom each morning at half past eight to chant " Onward Christian Soldiers " or " To Be a Pilgrim " more than half were girls of sixteen or more who were in their last year.

It seemed to me then that they had very splendid futures, these contemptuous blonde goddesses with their steady grey eyes and their arrogantly tossed pigtails. By day as a concession they wore the school uniform but at week-ends or in the holidays you saw them only in sweaters and well-cut tweeds. Then they were bound for the heath, carrying walking-sticks, along with their brothers or friends of their brothers, who almost always had fair hair and spoke in short clipped sentences. Usually there were spaniels or golden retrievers foraging in the bracken ahead of them and at intervals the girls would call something like " Come here, Prince," in high clear voices. Their fathers were on the Stock Exchange or imported things. From the road, walking with Lucy, I could never see the houses in which they lived. They were hidden from view along winding drives bordered by rhododendrons.

Very few of them had anything like a job in view, for then, even in our circle, that was regarded as a little daring. A girl might take a job, but as a diversion rather than as a necessity. A few were going on to study floral decoration and sometimes in

the main hall of St. Hilda's you would see a few of them with
Miss Debenham, whose uncle had known Sir John Millais,
conferring quietly over copper vases of lacquered beech leaves.
Some, again under Miss Debenham's guidance, were going on
to study interior decoration. Others would take art courses
(though not in Paris) and there were times when the green
lawns of St. Hilda's were dotted with solitary girls, stolid before
their easels, painting the ash grove that bordered the school
grounds.

Gracious, remotely smiling, her bangles giving out a little
chinking sound as she walked, Miss Debenham glided from easel
to easel, offering solace.

" How are we, Betty dear ? " she would ask in her sweet,
melancholy voice. "Do you feel *anything* coming through to you
yet, dear ? "

But these were in some ways the exceptions. Most often
you saw Mrs. Ogilvie waylay a senior girl after prayers to ask,
" As to your future, Mercia—have your parents decided ? "
And Mercia, for some reason colouring a little, would reply
almost as a set-piece : " Well, I'm going to stay at home and help
Mummy, Mrs. Ogilvie—for a bit at any rate."

I had not been at St. Hilda's long before I found there was
a catch to this. First, at prayers, Mrs. Ogilvie would make some
announcement that was far beyond me, full of phrases like
" felicitations " and " wish her every happiness in this blessed
state." While this went on I would be fiddling with some
treasure like a horse chestnut or an acid drop covered with fluff,
but once prayers finished the mistresses split up to descend on
the younger fry.

Usually it was someone like Miss Debenham whose faded
air of appeal was hard to resist. It went like this :

" Now, Dickie, you heard what Mrs. Ogilvie said, did you ?
No, well, perhaps you didn't quite understand, so I'll explain
—now you remember Mercia Elmbrook, who left just after you
came here ? I expect she was always very kind to you, wasn't
she? Oh—well, if she did, dear, it was only what you deserved,
because you're not supposed to run up the grass banks—I don't

suppose it was a very *hard* smack—well, now, Mrs. Ogilvie has heard quite by chance that Mercia is shortly to be married, so I'm sure you'd want to offer something from your pocket-money to help buy her a little something from all of us—just what you can spare, dear—well, no, a little more than a halfpenny——"

So no matter that I was adamant and insisted that I should have to ask my mother first—a penny, after all, bought a whole two ounces of bull's-eyes or aniseed balls. No matter that my mother, rummaging in her bag for stray silver, would mutter bitterly about "—absolute imposition—can't see why its *our* concern that the wretched girl's landed a husband." Mercia's wedding-present was assured, and that year's senior girls would feel, like Mercia, that there was a lot to be said for staying at home and helping Mummy.

So much for the Form IV girls. For the rest, the girls of Forms II and III, their ages ranged all the way from twelve to sixteen but there was nothing to be had there in the way of companionship. They spoke another language, a weird jargon of words like " swotting " and " prep " and " beastly impots " ; they jostled noisily in packs from classroom to netball field clutching ink-stained grammars, their swift whispered conclaves followed by pealing outbursts of laughter. Only Form I, the highest cell that any male of the species could attain among these worker queens, had forty or so girls of my own age—and they were a mixed bag indeed. There was Hazel, who met even well-merited reproof by dashing her pencil-box to the floor with a shout of " Silly old Ogilvie," finally to be carried from the school premises for ever, purple and screaming, tucked beneath her nanny's arm like a rolled umbrella. There was Veronica, who saw the issue of everything, exercise book or story primer, just as a challenge to her artistic powers and wrought havoc upon all of them, glugging industriously, with green and violet chalks. There were many ranging between these extremes, whose names I have forgotten. And there were five boys, including myself.

There was not much for me there either. Frankie, a rich importer's son, was really Hazel's male counterpart ; the slightest thwarting of his wishes reduced him to bestial grunts as he pounded his chubby fists on the desk-top like an outraged orang-utan. There was Michael, friendly enough and the only one among us to use hair-cream, but we trusted him less after his sly visits to Mrs. Ogilvie's study resulted in the discovery of plans to which he had been a party. There was Derek, timid and blinking, who claimed that his stepfather beat him twice a day, and there was Peter, muscular and boastful, who took Michael as his crony and was adept at twisting people's wrists behind the gymnasium until they sobbed for mercy. And there was me, numbed with dislike of it all.

For there was an ache to learn inside me like a hunger pain but the stifling dullness of that teaching would have made a dolt of any scholar. Not one of the staff—not Mrs. Ogilvie herself—so much as held a diploma for teaching. They had been brought up as ladies, they knew how to arrange flowers and paint pretty water-colours and they could talk parlour-French. For the rest, they taught from the book and from the book they could give you answers, but it was a sad day when you asked a question that the book did not cover. " You must wait until you're older," would be your answer then. Or " Little boys should pay attention to the lesson and not ask too many questions."

So I sat.

For three years I sat, hating it, and only the words of the Bible in Scripture lessons had any power to stir me. I hated the tedious genteel luncheons when Mrs. Ogilvie presided as head of the table, conducting an endless word game known as " Coffee-pots." I hated the physical training with Miss Kimberley, the instructor, coaxing us all to stand upright with her fluting cry of " Are we all tall ? " I hated every stone of the building, its red roofs and rough-cast walls, and the nannies and chauffeurs and the gleaming cars that gathered on the playground at four o'clock to bear their charges away.

Above all I hated the secrecy, the need to hide my feelings from my parents, in case they should worry, as carefully as ever they tried to keep their financial problems from me. And there was much to be kept dark.

After that bad beginning I wanted nothing more than to sink anonymously into that crowd like water into sand but it was not to be. So far as Mrs. Ogilvie was concerned, that first ill-timed start made me a marked man.

Of course I was no saint. Like all the other five-year-olds I was sometimes late, ran when I should have walked, banged desk-lids, left books lying about. For these sins of omission the others got reproofs, but they were rarely called out before the whole school after morning prayers. But if any of my sins reached Mrs. Ogilvie's ears I was called out, and often.

"This is Dickie Collier," she would inform the world at large in her deep purring voice. "I am not pleased with Dickie Collier."

This statement haunted me. It came at all times of the day—as I passed her in the entrance hall, booming down the lunch-table to interrupt a game of "Coffee-pots," even punctuating her tours of inspection with visiting parents. "This," she seemed anxious to assure them, "is not my ideal pupil. Please do not judge the standards of my school by *him*." But after prayers was worst because of the inquisition which followed.

"Speak up, Dickie. Louder, now—the whole school wants to hear—you have enough to say at other times, why not now? Wretched boy, will you speak up?"

At first she would accept no surrender less than tears and her victories were total, for what with the battery of stares and the muffled tittering, the tears came soon enough. Later, armed with flushed cheeks and stubborn silence, I learned to fight back; the inquisitions lasted longer now but I did not cry.

Where Mrs. Ogilvie led, Peter, the boastful and muscular one who was almost eight years old, was not slow to follow. He had long since tired of the fun of bullying Derek, who really must have spoken the truth about his stepfather; if Peter so much as approached to cuff him he hid his face and screamed heart-rendingly, like a rabbit in mortal terror. But I didn't scream and the first time Peter said something insulting about my mother I hit him smartly on the nose.

I suspect it was the only blow that did any damage. Peter

had elder brothers and had learned how to box. I had no elder brothers and I could not box—then. Three minutes later I went down for the fifth time and stayed there as still as a stone. I had hit my head on something and the sky and the clouds and the green leaves kept receding and coming back again. Just then the alarm bell went. The " tuck break " was over.

I could see Peter only with difficulty but the tone of his voice told me how scared he was. I must have been a sight for the gods.

" I say, look—you won't tell ? "

I shook my head faintly. I thought he meant Mrs. Ogilvie. I would tell her nothing under pain of death.

But he persisted. Fear was injecting false friendliness into his voice now. " You'll be a sport, won't you ? You won't tell your mother or anyone ? "

" 'Course not. Leave me alone, Peter. You're a rotter."

He said hastily, " I'll say you've been sick. I'll say you're in the loo. Then they won't come and look." Then he ran to be in class on time and left me on the gravel behind the gym.

Soon I was making a cautious way towards the cloakroom. But it troubled me, that frantic " You won't tell ? " I hated Peter, but now it dawned on me for the first time that if I told even my parents how much I hated him and why, it meant trouble for him. Peter was three years older than I was. If my face called for comment at home, I would have to lie and say I had fallen down.

All this I understood, more by instinct than by reason, but I hated it. It meant lying to my parents and before coming to Mrs. Ogilvie's I had always been able to tell them the truth. It was the first inevitable drawing apart that comes to all parents, all children, but I hated it.

In the tiled coolness of the washroom I splashed water on my stinging face. The voice came suddenly from behind me : " Turn round, Dickie Collier. Turn round and face me ! "

Drawn by the sound of running water when everyone else was in class, Mrs. Ogilvie had crept noiselessly down, as she often did, to investigate. And what she saw of my face told enough.

" You wicked little hooligan," she said between her teeth, " you've been brawling again."

Suddenly she laid hands on me. She laid her fat hands on me and she shook me until my stomach knotted up.

And I sensed that her self-control had almost gone because she was shouting over and over, " I don't want children like you in my school—I don't *want* them, do you hear me ? "

I felt her fingers biting into the flesh of my upper arms. With her face only a few inches from mine, I could see her thick lips parted and smell the bellodgia perfume she used, heavy-sweet and sickly on the warm air. There was a nameless terror in my mind then which clung to me over the years but, more than that a sadness at the loss of dignity, a sick sense of shame that human beings could feel a need to behave like this.

But as she led me by the ear towards my classroom I thought, well, at least the burden will be shared now. Even if it's only Peter I'll have a companion in adversity. I had not told her with whom I had fought. But when she put the question to the form, Peter would have to own up.

So it is sad to say that, after all, this detail slipped her mind. There was no sound in the classroom at all as I stood on the dais to receive the six stinging cuts from the ruler on the palm of my hand. But after that Mrs. Ogilvie seemed to lose interest in the affair and left the room. Justice had been done.

.   .   .

Even then, I think the vendetta might have died a natural death had it not been for the coming of Suzanne. And that made all things worse.

In Form I we had no news of her coming but then there was no reason why we should have done. She joined the class at the beginning of the summer term in 1930 when I was just six years old. Because of measles or something I was a day or two late returning and late for class into the bargain, but Miss Henslow was teaching so there was no trouble there. Just a quiet " Find a place quickly, Dickie," with no one so much as turning round because it was Scripture and Miss Henslow was telling us about the Good Samaritan.

There was the kind of hush in the classroom that you get in a forest when a wind has passed, because although she was not the best of teachers the wonder of that story has a power to subdue.

And I was quiet, listening with all the rest, until I saw her face.

She was in the front row, enthralled by the story, and she had no eyes for me then, but from the moment I saw her I had no ears for the story either. Better that Miss Henslow had been reading to us from the Song of Solomon for that was the way I felt now. " Thou art all fair, my love ; there is no spot in thee. . . ."

There is a kind of beauty that you would feel ashamed to touch, so fragile is it. And so it was with her. Curly hair the colour of a field of ripe wheat when the sun burnishes it and eyes a pale pale green, like a cat's eyes suddenly wakened from sleep. Yet when she laughed, which was often, and red lips parted to show tiny pearl-like teeth, those eyes came alive again as a cat's will and flashed their message to you—challenge, surrender, a rushing wave of emotions that I did not understand. And just to hear the cool huskiness of her voice speaking my name, I would feel weak and sick with everything turned topsy-turvy inside me.

Dear God, that was thirty years ago, yet this morning, remembering, it seems like yesterday.

Not that she knew what I felt then, unless by a kind of sixth sense, transmitted all the way across the room like wireless, because it was weeks before I spoke to her at all. For though I wanted to speak and tried to be near her in the playground and at other times, never a word could I find to say, and if she so much as glanced at me I could only scowl in return. The shyness reduced me to a quivering jelly.

If it had not been for Mrs. Ogilvie indeed we might never have known one another at all.

Strange that I never knew what started it all that terrible day. I had permission to get a drink of water, for the heat was fierce, and I had idled away ten pleasant minutes before I heard the shouting. It penetrated all the way to the cloakroom, so somebody was using their lungs full power.

But as I drew near the closed door of the classroom I stopped short. I knew who was shouting now. Mrs. Ogilvie . . . and in *our* classroom. She must have strode in, as she often did, to take over the lesson when I was out of the room.

Somebody else was getting the sharp edge of her tongue for once, but even listening I could feel sickness knotting my stomach. She was using words like swords, to wound and probe, and to a little girl by the sound of it. No words could have drowned that awful convulsive sobbing, which seemed to come from the very pit of the stomach.

Well, if I waited outside till she had finished, it would be my turn next. So I slipped in, anxious to gain my desk unseen.

But the moment I got inside I knew that I was not going to try and dodge trouble but to jump into it feet first. Because it was Suzanne up there, crying out in mortal terror like an animal that is hurt, her cheeks all scarlet and her little hands bunched into fists, knuckling the tears from her eyes.

All day I had stolen glances at her, as at a goddess, in her sky blue dress and little white ankle socks rolled neatly above white kid shoes, but she did not look like a goddess now. She looked stripped and humiliated, as if this savagery had torn all her defences aside.

And suddenly it was as if I was not there at all but in a far-off place where I had never been and the roaring in my ears was the clash of steel and the neighing of horses and the cries of the dying across a green meadow stained bright with blood. Someone began shouting : " Dirty old witch . . . let her alone ! Beastly old bully ! "

The shock I had, to come to and realise that it was me.

But then pandemonium broke out and there was no stopping it. First Hazel began to scream, because Hazel could always scream on principle and in a minute other children had taken it up, screaming and crying, and soon Frankie reverted to the jungle again, beating his fists and bellowing. Miss Henslow, who was in charge, seemed to be speaking a piece of her mind to Mrs. Ogilvie, and what was more, Mrs. Ogilvie, seeing she had gone too far now, took it like a lamb. Suddenly in all the confusion Suzanne turned and ran—past Mrs. Ogilvie, past me and out of the door—scarlet and tear-streaked, the sobs still tearing her like spasms. Out of the main door and across the playground and suddenly, despite the shouts to come back, I was running too.

I found her under the gymnasium. The funny thing is that I knew where to look, because I had hidden there myself during "tuck breaks" when I wanted to keep out of Peter's way. But no one else knew this, and only the instinct of the hunted could have taken her there. The gymnasium was a big wooden building raised from the ground and if you crawled in under the supports it was too dark for anyone to see you without the help of a torch.

But when I did find and touch her she only wept harder, crying over and over, "Oh, let me alone . . . I want to go home . . . I want to go home." That was what I thought she said, but tears jumbled up the words so that I could only guess. It was so awful it tore at my heart.

So for the moment I left her, but only to go in search of something that would stop those tears. I felt responsible, like any lover, yet I had so little to offer. The only thing I could think of was to crawl out covered with cobwebs and away to the meadow nearby, doubling in and out of the shrubbery so that no one would see. And there I picked her the best bouquet that I could find, though it seemed poor enough—dandelions, buttercups, pink and white campions with a sprig of purple vetch for good measure. Clutching them tightly I crept back to her.

Now the sobbing had subsided a little and my flowers seemed to do the trick. She blinked tears from her eyes, blew her nose and looked at them. A shaft of daylight came in so that I could see her face and the beginning of a smile. She said, "For me?" and I swallowed hard and said yes. Then she looked at me and said, "Why, Dick?" very quietly in the way she had and I thought, Oh, here it comes, I've got to say it. So I just said, " 'Cos I love you," but it cost me the seven years I had lived to say it and I couldn't meet her eyes.

And all at once, she was smiling through tears and trying not to snuffle, and saying, "I think you're nice. Not like the others. I like you heaps better than them." And I said, " I thought you might not. I thought you might think I was silly. Will you marry me ? "

This she considered very gravely, but she didn't laugh, as I'd been afraid she would. Instead she said, " Yes, I think I will. At least if you want me to. I s'pose I ought to think about it, 'cos the girl has to, but I know I want to so I can't see why I have to think."

Then she held the flowers to her tightly and said, " That means we're engaged and it's all right for you to kiss me. But you needn't if you don't want."

But I did want. So we knelt upright in the dust beneath the gym and her face, despite the tears, was cool to the touch. Not so her lips. They lit a fire in me like a match put to paper and I was anywhere but St. Hilda's on a summer afternoon, just putting off the moment when the ruler would cut into my palms. Presently we went back to face the music though after that it never seemed to matter.

Ah, Suzanne.

.   .   .

Next morning Suzanne's father paid a call on Mrs. Ogilvie. I did not see him but they said he came in a great gleaming car driven by a chauffeur and trailed a blue scarf of cigar smoke behind him as he walked. The upshot was that Suzanne got an abject apology and after that Mrs. Ogilvie could never do enough for her.

As for me, I was " in Coventry " and I stayed there for three weeks. A desk apart, right out in front, under the mistresses' eye ; an empty place on either side of me at meal-times to emphasise my apartness, like Ishmael in the book of Genesis. Of course, the mistresses could have spoken to me if they wanted, but none of the others could, under penalty of the same fate—not even Suzanne. I had behaved, as Mrs. Ogilvie announced, " like a blackguardly butcher's boy," in calling her names.

But I didn't mind. I could look at Suzanne and she could look at me. They couldn't stop us doing that.

By the time the " Coventry " ended I think people had forgotten that I *could* talk, for they never bothered me much after that. For about a year Suzanne and I were separate and self-contained amidst them all, two against the world.

We shared the same books—*Winnie the Pooh* still stood at the top of the list, with *Black Beauty* and *Treasure Island* close behind and *The Magnet* and *The Gem* both highly favoured for everyday reading. And, so far as you can ever tell with a woman, we shared the same thoughts.

Our games, too, became something of a ritual—in the " tuck break " behind the gym, in the meadows at lunch-time. There, by the kind of instinct that knows what is painful to another we learned to compromise. Girls, I knew, liked to play " House," a game I had always scorned, though I consented to play " House " with Suzanne. But there were difficulties.

" Now it's six o'clock," Suzanne would say, " you can come home from business now."

So I would say, " All right. Are you coming to meet me at the station ? "

" Silly ! You don't come by train, you come by car. Jenkins is driving you."

" Who's Jenkins ? "

" He's our chauffeur—at home—but *we've* got him now. He's putting the car away now so you can give me a kiss."

" All right. Now can I put my feet up ? "

" 'Course not. I told you, it's six o'clock. I'll shake you a cocktail then you must change for dinner. And I'll tell you about all the new dresses I've bought and you can tell me about how tired you are and the bulls and bears."

" What are bulls and bears ? "

" They're things you sell—at least I *think* that's what they are. . . ."

Soon, by common consent, we had stopped playing " House."
It underlined too many of the differences between our ways of
life—differences which didn't seem to matter so long as you
didn't think about them. I never protested in so many words
that my father travelled by train and not by chauffeur-driven car,
that he enjoyed a glass of sherry before his dinner but thought
that cocktails were the invention of the devil, that he might
change into a velvet smoking-jacket but never a dinner-jacket
and that he didn't sell animals for a living. Suzanne knew and so
did I. Better to play games that were rooted in common ground.

So our make-believe had an ivory-tower quality and in an
English meadow bright with buttercups a small boy in grey
flannel shorts and a little girl in a flounced dress became highway-
man and proud heiress, buccaneer and governor's daughter,
outlaw chief and baron's unhappy ward. Or—closer to home
because we both dipped into magazines our parents left lying
around—titled private detective, in full evening dress, rescuing
beautiful heiress, also in full evening dress, from an opium den
in the East End of London. Once I was a Harley Street surgeon
who performed an intricate operation on Suzanne's teddy-bear
and said gravely, " Your son will live."

Because of her I dreamed great dreams—sinful expansive,
deliciously impossible, dreams. I was going to write books—
that was suddenly settled at the age of seven. They were going
to make a lot of money—that had become essential too. To
achieve this I would only write about people who drank cocktails
and wore evening dress all day. We would live in a house with a
staff including nine gardeners who presented spades on inspection
each morning—something like the Changing of the Guard. We
would have two Rolls-Royces and be on nodding terms with every
head waiter on the French Riviera. Thus will a seven-year-old
dream for the woman he loves.

Outside St. Hilda's we scarcely saw one another at all. Once
or twice she came to tea but it was less of a success. She lived
five miles distant and our parents did not " know " one another.
Each day at four the great grey car, gleaming like a gun-carriage,
collected her and bore her away. Once Suzanne prevailed upon

Jenkins to give me a lift but that was hardly a success either. He did not open the door to usher me inside and bow low. He said, " Hop in smartly, nipper, and keep those boots off the seat."

As will happen time and again, the day that dawned with the brightest promise was the day that ended as grey as twilight.

It was the day of the big cricket match and, quite independently, the day when we decided to run away.

It wasn't a match either of us had any interest in but it must have meant something to St. Hilda's because we had all been given a half-holiday to watch. Our senior girls were playing some other senior girls and there was bunting hanging all over the playground in honour of it but all the juniors were just by the side of the playing-fields, chewing grass and talking quietly.

Both of us were as low as could be because that morning Mrs. Ogilvie had called me to her study and told me that I was to stop keeping company with Suzanne. To this day I don't know why—except that when all was said and done she had the mind and tongue of an adder. But she didn't volunteer an explanation. " This undesirable friendship must cease."

We talked it over in the sunshine with the smell of the cut grass and just the *chock* of the ball as background and suddenly it all came boiling up inside me like milk on a stove and I said, " I'm going to run away. But only if you'll come too,"

And to my surprise she got up without a murmur and said, " All right. When ? "

So I set my lips and said, " Now. While old Ogilvie's not watching."

Just then somebody was caught out or something because there was an " Ooh ! " and a lot of applause and while that was distracting them all we wriggled away on our stomachs, through sweet-scented grass until we came to the boundary fence where there was a loose plank. I helped her through and there we were at the edge of a wood that we had never explored before. Then we stopped, hearts thumping with the sense of our own daring, and said, " What now ? "

And I decided, " If we go far enough this way we ought to reach the sea. Then we might get a boat."

Did I think there was a chance that we might somehow get a boat and sail away from it all like the Owl and the Pussy-Cat? I look back and I can no longer say with certainty how I reasoned it. I only know what we did. At first we set off with purpose, for the wood was a green twilit world, mercifully cool and starred with white scented drifts of woodruff. Presently though, we reached a field and the going was rougher, for the grass grew only in coarse tufts and the earth was rutted and uneven, baked brown the colour of pottery. We stumbled on but though Suzanne was trying to be brave about it I could see that her feet were in agony. Those delicate white kid shoes had never been made for this kind of country.

We seemed to have been trudging for hours stumbling over ruts and pricking ourselves on thistles and getting nettle-rashed into the bargain when Suzanne said: " Do you think we could buy some lemonade? I'm *so* thirsty."

A chill went through me—the first of many such as an escort of limited means—for I realised that I had brought no money. But I said, more confidently than I felt, " I'd better get you some water from a house. They have to give it to you by law."

After that hours seemed to go by. We did come to a road at last but we were dusty and sore-footed and parched with thirst by the time we got to it. The first gate we came to a great dog came and barked furiously so we ran away. At the second a gardener lifted his head from his digging and said, " 'Op it ! " He didn't seem to know about the law.

Then there were hundreds of miles of road that threw up clouds of snowy white dust and a brassy sun glaring from a cruel sky until suddenly I stopped short and said faintly : " Oh, golly."

" What's the matter ? "

" We . . . I . . . I think we've walked in a sort of circle. I think in just a minute. . . ."

And we had. We rounded a corner and there, only a few hundred yards away, were the sprawling red roofs and the creeper-covered walls. We were back at St. Hilda's.

Inside me I struggled whether to be glad or sorry—glad

because I was hot and tired and wanted my tea, sorry because I felt I had failed and my masculinity was in the dust, along with my boots. But as to Suzanne—well, there was no doubting how *she* felt. She tidied her hair. She looked at her tiny delicately-modelled wrist-watch. She said, " Goodness, it's four o'clock—the car will be here. I'll be late."

And as we drew nearer we saw the car indeed was there—long, gleaming, arrogant. But not only Jenkins was in attendance to-day. A man and woman were standing there, glancing impatiently up the school drive as the children streamed out. The strange thought crossed my mind that both of them *belonged* to the car—the imperative way the man held his head, lips pursed below the moustache, as if life was a servant that was keeping him waiting. The woman with her beautifully-cut costume, the material lustrous and soft, the carefully-waved platinum hair, the mouth a scarlet slash of discontent.

Suzanne gave a cry. " It's Mummy and Daddy . . . I *must* rush," then turned to me, " Why, what's the matter ? " I was biting my lip, trying not to cry. I knew I would cry when she was gone, but I was not going to let her have the satisfaction now. I said, "You don't care . . . it was all just a game to you. You didn't mean to run away at all." Such dishonesty, when I too wanted my tea—but how could she be so matter-of-fact ?

Then I felt cruel because suddenly she hugged me and the green eyes enslaved me and she said, " Dick, don't spoil it . . . it *has* been lovely . . . and I *do* love you best. Only I'll have to run away another day because Mummy's got people coming to tea." Then she kissed me. Then she was gone. For the first time I had come face-to-face with the devastating practicality of woman, who can ascend to Olympus for eternity but always remembers to come down in time for tea.

I saw her fleeting up the road towards them and I felt even then, without knowing why, that she had gone away from me for ever. As I came level Suzanne did pause in her apologies to say, " Mummy, this is Dick." But her mother wasn't listening. She was saying something about, " Darling, it is rather tedious of you . . ." Her parents looked through me. Both of them.

Right through me. If someone had slapped me across the face to bring tears it could not have hurt more just then.

Two days later the school broke up and by autumn we were both at different schools. Of course every tragedy in that springtime of life is the end of the world, and we get over all of them so quickly. But who says we forget?

CHAPTER SIX

MY FATHER'S GARDEN

---

*I value my garden more for being full of
blackbirds than of cherries, and very frankly
give them fruit for their songs*

JOSEPH ADDISON

WELL, IT was a good thing there was plenty doing in that time
of St. Hilda's, for in youth a new diversion is like a curtain to be
drawn across sadness. In those days the greatest diversion was
my father's garden. For years, week in, week out, we heard of
little else.

Of course, the garden had been taking shape ever since I was
born but my father's decision to wall himself in only really
became of first importance in the spring of 1930. Goodness
knows, it seems harmless enough that a young man should have
called " Good morning " over the hedge to my father, who was
plucking a rose ; in any case he had only rented the house next
door for three months. But my father did not know this and he
saw it as the beginning of the end. " This place is getting like
an Eastern bazaar," he said, as he came indoors pale with anger,
" You can't move a step without being accosted."

Not that my father was an unsociable man when the time and
the place were ripe. A cup of hot tea with the vicar at eleven,
to mull over England's prospects in the Test Match, was to him
the breath of life. But the yearning to roam his own acres
unregarded, free from curious eyes, crumbling the loose soil in
his fingers, was as deep-rooted in him as in most Englishmen.

So must the yeomen, dust now in the churchyard on the hill, have felt as they walked this valley in the first Elizabeth's time.

For now my father began quite literally to hedge himself in. Determined to enjoy " an Englishman's right to seclusion," he had to deny himself the secret pleasure of watching his trees and shrubs gain height year by year. As the long summer evenings drew on, my father took to the woods with a wheel-barrow to root up fully grown elders and dog roses, replanting them by moonlight in our front garden. And hawthorns and maple and privet and box were set to join them, until we were surrounded by a wall of greenery ten feet high. In summer this not only shut off all view of the neighbours but of the railway station, the farm on the hill and the church spire. But now, at last, my father breathed a sigh of relief. His privacy was assured.

I must tell you how he planned that garden. Above all, it was a garden made to surprise you, half cultivated, half wild, with delightful unexpected twists and turns wherever you thought to go. You saw it at its best on a warm April morning when the sun had not yet burned the dew from the orchard grass, a heat-hazy day when the light was as if an artist's brush had coloured all the far horizon with a faint blue wash. On a morning like that you could stand under a white pyramid of pear blossom, or, beneath the pink, tight, still unbroken buds of apple trees and smell the salt of the sea drifting from miles away on a faint west wind. And the earth of the kitchen garden, if the rains had not come, would be a dusty biscuit brown in the morning light. But at evening, after a shower had passed, you saw the thin green of spring seeds pricking the dark metallic-smelling earth—carrots and onions and turnips and the coiling spirals of the new peas.

North of the house, beyond the main shrubbery, the lawns stretched away as green and clipped as a cricket pitch, bordered by the pink foam of flowering cherry and the clean white peeling columns of birch trees . . . Thus far all was formal, but once beyond the hedge where the honeysuckle twined, you were in a wild exciting world. May trees and elders made cool, vaulted oases of shade at the edge of the orchard grass and your nostrils prickled with the thick mushroomy smell of leaf-mould and the farmyard reek of well-rotted dung. Then suddenly the shade was gone and from then on all the way was sunlight, right to where the kitchen garden stood with the bees noisy among the scarlet runners. But there was nothing dull about the route you took, for here the wild flowers brightened the way, where my father had set them. Primroses peeped demurely from the grass, and in spring, you saw the dark trumpets of bluebells carpeting the hedgerow, vying with frail green tassels of dog's mercury.

For me a garden must delight the nose no less than the eye —so I had no quarrel with my father there. At breakfast time in summer, the sweet muskiness of clove pinks drifted on waves of heat through the open dining-room windows, and only a stone's throw away stood the rose garden, the blooms pale gold, snow white and church-cassock crimson, smooth, velvety and wine-smelling in the early sunlight. Those tiny tightly-rolled buds formed my father's buttonhole in the days when buttonholes were fashionable, and each morning, on his arrival at the office, the Government messenger's first duty was to bring two drinking glasses—one for my father's carafe, one for that morning's rose.

But all that garden was an intoxication of scent : the apricot perfume of wallflowers, the tiny white bells of lily-of-the-valley, hyacinths, pink, white and blue, like encrustations of coral, and, in the evening, the peppermint smell of catmint and the cold sweet odour of nicotianas, looming like pale moons in the dusk. As for the colours, they seemed to range through the whole palette, from the dark, still columns of the cypress through the rich russet of copper beech to the palest grey of lichens crusting gnarled apple branches. Everywhere colour changed with season, the rich blue spikes of delphinium succeeding the guinea-gold of daffodils with the soaring trunks of the beech trees, silver-grey like cathedral arches, as immutable background to it all.

Of course a symphony needs sound effects but these we had too. Bird song from sunrise to sunset—the cheeky twitter of sparrows, a blackbird's liquid cadence, the poignant monotony of the cuckoo, on and on with the muted whirr of a lawn-mower as descant. The quiet sad sighing of the poplars down the long lane that led away from the house. And many moments when sight, scent and sound could together say as much as the words of the greatest poets.

Take the scent of white lilac, after rain on a spring evening, see the flower sprays against the twilight with the delicate green of foliage and listen as the deep iron music of church bells is borne across the valley—— That is a memory to hold fast to the heart, come what may.

Autumn, too, was rich in such moments, when the long shadows barred the stubble fields, and the rooks corkscrewed and cried above. Now our potatoes were all harvested, row after row of King Edwards spaced neatly on the dark turned earth, and September sun struck warm on the bronzed bruised green of tomatoes ripening on our southern wall. The leaves that drifted from the branches held the amber colour of wet wood-shavings, and this was the time of bonfires.

Why are a boy and his father so close when a bonfire is lit? The reason eludes me even now. It is a secret moment, almost one of ritual, when no one says much because so much is understood. First the exciting moments, when the flames are red and yellow, leaping and snapping and you can see the sparks and smuts drifting off through almost bare branches towards the pale face of the moon.

But the best comes after, when you realise that Vulcan can truthfully be a peaceful god. There is no sound from the bonfire at all, though the inside of it is all red and lambent and gently glowing, as if the fire-god was breathing easily, digesting his meal. Somewhere in the embers potatoes are baking in their jackets and you can feel the water gathering in your mouth at the thought of how soon you will be splitting one lengthways with your new pocket-knife, to watch the mist of heat arise before setting a chunk of fresh farm butter to melt on the hot sweet flesh.

In a moment you bite, scalding your tongue if you are not careful, and as you nibble, there is the bitter-sweet tang of wood smoke all about you. Smoke, yellow and grey, is purling slowly away from the cone of the fire, and a little breeze stirs the leaves, expressing the faint sigh of peace that is inside you unuttered.

Now you know that you have done all you can, that the fire will stay in, yet somehow you linger. You stare intently at the glowing core, as if trying to read some message from it. That is the thrall of the fire as if man and boy, in an autumn garden were close to something primordial then—given up to the long groping thoughts that men have had round camp-fires at night since the world began.

Still, that is past.

.   .

When it came to his garden, my father's passions were easily aroused. He knew every one of his roses by name; to him with his gentleness and sensibility they were all people. "I'm very worried about Mrs. Henry Morse," he would say after finding a trace of black spot on one of them. "She's not looking at all well this morning." Once I remember, Mr. Crombie, a great man living nearby, who was secretly impressed by my father's roses, invited him on a conducted tour of *his* rose garden.

My father was not, I realise now, too well off at the time; a little envy would have been human. Yet he came back smoking with disgust for quite another reason. It was some time before he could find breath to say, " I wouldn't be in that fellow's shoes for all the tea in China."

" Why not ? " my mother asked, probably knowing full well but giving her cue, as a good wife will.

" Do you know how many of those roses he knew by name ? " my father asked in tones of measured contempt. " Out of all those bushes ? Not one ! He had to send for his gardener every time I asked a name. A rich man and a company director, indeed ! What good does all that money do him ? If he doesn't even think of his roses as human, I'm sorry for his staff."

Now this made me quiet and uncomfortable, for I was just then planning great things for Suzanne and myself, but it made me think a bit, now and since. And in time of course I knew my father was right, for there was no gold anywhere that could have bought the way he felt about his flowers.

I must admit though that he had his prejudices. Just as he wanted his furniture to symbolise simplicity and " loving kindness," so it was with the garden. Roses were all very well, but if a weed flourished here and there in the rose garden, my father was the first man to welcome it and let it be. " There's room for all of them in this garden," he told me once, " These are the waifs of the hedgerows and I'm not going to throw them out."

" You know, even the weeds are human to him," my mother said once as we watched from the bedroom window, but her forbearance was to make a rod for her own back. It was not long afterwards that she found my father with a trowel, firming the earth round a newly-planted clump of nettles.

" Charles," she said, her voice grown a shade high, " why in Heaven's name are you planting those ? "

It was really beyond my father's power to tell her. Instead the far-away look came over his face that was always there when he was espousing a lost cause. " They're so simple," was all he could say.

They certainly added an original touch to a common-or-garden flower bed but my mother never saw it that way. At intervals I heard from her about those nettles for years.

There were other flowers which to him symbolised sophistication and opulence that he would not even give border room. For a time my mother toyed with the idea of a tulip border just inside the front gate and even old Mr. Wade avowed that " there weren't nothing so fine as a bed of tulips, all red and gold, standing up straight there like soldiers on parade." But my father said almost fiercely that there was no loving kindness in a tulip and that ended the matter.

It was the same with every living thing in that garden. In some years we went short of cherries and raspberries for my father would never have them netted, even when the birds were among them from morning to night. He said that the birds could so easily break a leg if they got entangled in the netting.

" We can buy cherries if we want them," he said, leaving

87

unexplained why he had planted the trees in the first place, " You can't buy a blackbird's song."

And of course he was right. There were times when your feet crunched all day on the tiny polished stones that were the birds' leavings but we had a pæan of bird song in which to glory all the year round, as if they were giving thanks to my father, their protector and friend.

Not every one of our gardeners saw it his way, mind you. They were all for netting the fruit bushes and for purging every flower bed of weeds so that they would compare with a public park for primness. But this was not my father's way, though his desire to " help the underdog " led him to give jobs to gardeners who very plainly would never stay the course. So many were there that I have forgotten the names of most, though I do remember Arthur, who terminated his contract by the unusual method of lobbing a dead starling through the dining-room window, remarking casually " Present for yer." And there was Ebenezer, whose one sullen delight was to hose down the garage week after week, making it spotless and shining in readiness for the car that my father never bought. "I'll wet your socks," he would scream shrilly to anyone whose approach seemed likely to curb his joy.

All these came in quick succession after old Mr. Wade had left us, and that is a day I will never forget. That was another day I saw my father in a light that made me swell with pride, then and for years after.

I was at St. Hilda's then, I know, for sometimes in the morning I would leave the house with my father and walk with him as far as the station before going on up to the school. Most often we would meet old Mr. Wade at the bottom of the lane, on his way to begin his day's work.

Old Mr. Wade was in tune with my father's thoughts and ways. Side by side they would stand together, quietly conferring for half an hour at a time, rapt with the wonder of what they were creating. His blood was rich with old traditions. To him there was only one way to nourish the soil—with wood ash and farm manure. There was but one way of digging—to a fork's

depth. For years, whenever he occupied the seat of honour at
the Working Men's Club, men had hung on his words, jealous
for a scrap of advice on conquering turnip-fly, absurdly proud if
that year's leeks merited his praise.

So much that was in my father's mind Mr. Wade understood.
He did not want to see the fruit bushes netted. The birds were
his friends too. Each morning he would bring a paper bag
of crumbs to feed the robins that hopped after him up and
down the rows. His triumph was when one flew to his very
fingertips to take crumbs, small black beady eyes watching him
knowingly.

" Ain't he a caution ? " he rumbled then, a slow grin lighting
up his face, " Look at him now—two pennorth of sauce ? "

For all his gruff voice and his burly frame, he was a gentle
man. He could fork over a patch of ground in a trice, yet still
leave intact the tiny red flowers of the Scarlet Pimpernel that he
and my father loved. " 'E's your sundial," he would say,
pointing. " Just watch him now. See 'im close his flowers up,
means we're going to 'ave storm." When my mother brought
him a cup of tea or told him his lunch was ready, he would
sweep off his tweed cap like some grizzled old courtier : " Thank
you, marm. I take that very kindly."

And in the way of the old countrymen he would touch his
cap to my father each morning, not in a servile way like a man
currying favour but the sturdily independent gesture of a man
who knew himself to be as good as you but who still touched
his cap as a mark of respect to a good guv'nor.

But that morning, as our feet scuffed up the white dust of
the lane and we saw Mr. Wade coming from a long way off, we
knew something was wrong.

He was staring straight ahead of him, like a man demented,
and his feet were faltering all over the road as if the sun had
struck him. And in some way that made me prickle all over like
a dog scenting trouble he was different. The old tweed cap,
the ruddy cheeks and honest blue eyes, the clipped sergeant-
major's moustache—they were the same. Yet it was like seeing
a waxwork figure of a man walk up that lane, endowed with the

same features, dressed in the same clothes, yet feeling it was not the man at all.

If he saw us as he came close, it made no difference. His right hand was not going up to his cap this morning. Both his hands hung loosely at his sides, the fingers outspread. I felt a sick horror engulfing me. It is an awful thing, at seven years old to see an adult, and one who has always made you quake a bit, suffering the agonies of the damned and no longer caring how they look.

Like that he stood before us, seeing us and yet not seeing us, the grief producing strange strangled sounds in his throat, and my father said, " Well, now, Mr. Wade . . ."

For the space of a second there was only the sunlight and the appalling sounds, then with a rush it came out: " Proper ashamed, sir, you seeing me like this . . . but it's my wife, you see . . . she *died* this morning." All his face broke up then and he could say no more but something like a low howl came out of him.

Now I will say without fear of contradiction that there was no fairer man in the world than my father. You knew where you were with him and I can believe he never told a lie or said a hurtful thing in all his life. But like most Englishmen of his age and class he could be a little formal and reserved with people he knew only just so well. If he was just, he was also aloof.

Yet here he was now, while I stood open-mouthed, with his arm round the old man's shoulders and murmuring the words of comfort that one old friend might use to another : " Buck up, old chap . . . yes, I know it's hard . . . better get back home now and get some rest . . . I know, yes, I know."

Suddenly old Mr. Wade cried out, " It was forty years, sir . . . forty years together . . . *why* did she have to go away ? " His face worked with grief and the tears rolled unchecked down his cheeks and though he tried to get his breath he couldn't. There was only that strangled choking sound, cross between a sigh and a groan. But my father just stood there in his dark business suit with the rose in his buttonhole, never taking his arm from round the old man's shoulders, and from time to time he patted him absently as a man will do when he seeks for more words of comfort and knows that none of them can help.

And presently the old man subsided, his blue eyes red-rimmed with sorrow and he took his great red bandanna hankerchief from his pocket and blew his nose. That was when my father said quite firmly, "Get along home now, Mr. Wade . . . get some sleep. Lucy'll let us know when you feel like coming again."

It was almost brisk and matter-of-fact, yet it was what was needed. It did the trick. The old man mumbled and touched his cap but as he shuffled off his gait was brisker. He was master of himself again.

In some strange way, though, the cord was broken. We heard from Lucy that " Dad was going to take it easy for a bit and see how he got on." But the weeks and the months went by and he did not return. We sensed that he was slipping into a decline, broken by his grief. Within a year he had gone to join her.

And I, too young to understand the nature of an immortal love between the gruff old man and the hunched grey-haired little woman with bird-bright eyes whom I just knew as Lucy's mother, strove hard to rationalise it and could not then. Did love go on like that even when you were as old as they? And wherein lay the bond, that my father should have wept at his passing and said, " He was a great gentleman. It was a privilege to have employed him."

Yet I think now that the bond was the garden to which they had given their hearts.

.   .   .

As to the apple trees, my father was always dubious about pruning them, wondering whether they were in some way sensible of the pruning knife, and some of the branches eventually grew to sixteen feet in length. On bitter winter nights he would wander uneasily round those trees in a top-coat, fearful lest the first frosts should nip them in the bud, and in the spring, when the whole orchard was misty-white with blossom, his feelings would so overcome him that he would skip a pace or two, snapping his fingers with delight.

Now it was always understood that an orchard would form part of our garden, but just how large a part my mother never realised until too late. All the ordering of the trees and shrubs was my father's prerogative when they moved in, and it was only a little after that my mother thought to ask how many fruit trees would be coming.

" I ordered forty," my father said, busy with his pipe, " just for a start."

My mother almost drove the darning needle through her thumb. " Forty . . . *forty apple trees*. You ordered *forty apple trees* ? "

" Some are plum," said my father, as if that altered everything, " and a few pear. We couldn't use forty apple trees."

" But we could use forty fruit trees, I suppose," said my mother, ready to fly at him. " What are we going to do with them ? With the fruit, I mean."

My father pretended to consider this a while. " Well," he said, as if this clinched the argument, " they'll come in useful for jam."

Next day, before my mother could countermand the order from the nursery, they arrived. Miserable-looking switches of stick, they were, done up in damp sacking, with a few trailing roots attached. They looked so harmless my mother relented there and then.

My father planted every one himself, spading deep down into the heavy orange clay of the pasture. Then he mulched them with barrow-loads of manure and well-rotted grass cuttings. When the weather turned dry he watered them by hand.

And his touch was magical. They grew. They flourished. Within a year or two the silver-green leaves and the pale pink blossom were everywhere. My mother held her breath, waiting.

And still the trees grew. They began to bear fruit. Green shining Bramley Seedlings that would keep and sweet purple-black Carlsbad plums that would not. Damsons, blue-black and tart, pale Codlins, glowing red Worcester Pearmains, crisp, nutty Cox's Orange Pippins. Crab apples and yellow syrupy Marie Louise pears.

In the autumn the grass came alive with black and yellow wasps and the air resounded to their droning. The starlings chattered from morning to night. But an army of birds and insects could have made no impression there.   In one year we harvested thousands of bushels of apples, more than a hundred pounds of plums, to say nothing of raspberries, black-currants and gooseberries. Meanwhile, along the orchard hedge, there were ripe blackberries waiting to be picked.

My father took time off from the office. " It would be a pity to waste them," he said, " and you, my son, can lend a hand."

Each morning, early, armed with ladders and baskets, we set off for the orchard. We picked until we were drugged with the smell of ripe fruit. We sweated in the topmost boughs, the wasps buzzing resentfully round our heads, the bitter-rough smell of tree bark in our nostrils. At intervals my mother brought us trays of tea and lemonade.

" But Charles," she said once, trying to keep reasonableness in her voice, " you don't eat fruit. Hardly ever. You say it upsets your stomach."

" Other people like it," my father said, conjuring visions of a whole army of dependants waiting at our door.

My mother raised her eyes heavenwards. " Never mind about other people. What are *we* going to do with it ? Until you've made up your mind I can't plan my day."

Silence for a moment. When my father spoke again, even the height of the ladder on which he stood was no help in maintaining the dignity he sought to achieve. " I think," he said, " it would be a good idea to store it—some of it anyway. Or bottle it. I don't know. I had no idea everyone would raise such difficulties over my growing a little fruit."

In this moment my father stood revealed for what he was— a dreamer of dreams. If the question of what he was going to do with the fruit once he had grown it ever crossed his mind, he had long ago dismissed it. In a vision he had seen himself in an

93

orchard to shame the finest, monarch of every ripe red apple he surveyed. Now the dream had become reality he had to confess the awful truth. He had no plans for disposal.

For days after that, morning, afternoon and evening, my mother was busy bottling fruit. The sickly sweet smell of boiling jam and heated iron spread through the whole house. She pulped fruit ; she turned fruit into flans and pies and tarts and turnovers. Even now, looking back to boyhood, I can feel the spittle coming into my mouth at the thought of my mother's blackberry pies, crust and cream and wine-dark juice all blending into a timeless mouth-watering ecstasy between teeth and tongue.

But even then there was fruit to spare. My mother invited people she didn't want to tea if only they would take pity on us and carry away a basketful of apples—or better still fill the boot of their car to overflowing. The house smelt like a Covent Garden warehouse with all the boxes of apples we had packed neatly away into odd corners. Every window-sill and shelf and cupboard bore its load of apples, polished to a turn, awaiting their fate, sitting smugly like so many unwelcome guests who know you can do nothing about their presence.

Sometimes, when my mother waxed most eloquent on their presence, my father felt constrained to apologise. " It would be a pity to waste them," he said to no one in particular.

This went on for ten long years. To me it always seemed the moment to tiptoe tactfully from the room.

Yet human nature is funny. Years later, when he had gone, and his apples were no longer something you could joke about, I paid a visit home one day to find my mother tired almost to weeping. The war years were past, when you would find people ready to take the fruit away by the bushel, yet, uncannily, there they all were, just like the old days. Shelf after shelf, sill after sill ranged with neatly polished apples, and the sweet familiar smell everywhere— and now I began to see why my mother was tired.

It must have taken her literally weeks to gather them in like this, alone and unaided, and she had sent no word that she needed help.

"But why?" I asked, "I . . . well, I always thought that you couldn't bear the sight of them."

And her lip trembled a little as she replied, "It's a pity to waste them when they're there. That's what your father would have said, isn't it? And I think he'd have liked to see them, poor darling. Come on now and get your tea."

CHAPTER SEVEN

A QUESTION OF VALUES

A great devotee of the Gospel of Getting On
GEORGE BERNARD SHAW

BUT DESPITE all the joys of our garden, it took time to get over Suzanne. I had gone from St. Hilda's and a full year was past before I did. Perhaps it seems stupid to say that a child could be in love but only I know how it felt and it did not seem stupid then. I would have died for her once, though it is strange to think of now.

The only bit of good cheer I had was my last school report, or the part that was left blank for the headmistress to comment on "Progress" and "Conduct." In that space, as a parting shot, Mrs. Ogilvie had written in all seriousness, "Dickie and I are not friends." My father and mother laughed so much when they read this, the tears started to their eyes.

Bit by bit, then, the story of the past three years came out, and my father was all for going up and having it out with Mrs. Ogilvie right away. But I managed to talk him out of it on the understanding that if anything like that happened again I was never to hold it back.

Of course, I did, though it was never so bad, because I couldn't help remembering what my father had said years back. "*Anything you want to do you'll mostly have to do yourself.*" It seemed a good plan to stick to that, both in work and play, and not to go bringing parents into it, because you see one day there would be the house. And that seemed like luck enough for one boy.

So I relied on myself if troubles came, then and always, and at Waterton House School for Boys I was working hard and winning scholarships and exhibitions but I thought too often about Suzanne for my peace of mind.

I thought I had found the answer as to why her parents had looked through me like that, the answer to why I had lost her. And the answer was money.

I didn't believe I would have any money for years and years. I didn't believe I would ever see Suzanne again, and I was right. But the black heresy I was coming to believe was that money was the only thing in life worth the having. You could do anything if you had money. You could marry a girl like Suzanne. They couldn't touch or hurt you or look right through you if you just had the money.

Perhaps the district was making its mark on me too. Little by little it was changing and money was changing it. The builders were moving in to the hills beyond the valley, across the chalky rabbit-cropped turf where the wild thyme and the gentians grew. In those fields, seven years back, Lucy had pushed my pram each afternoon, but you could not push a pram there now. Instead they were pushing cement-mixers and dredgers for the houses that were springing up on every hand. Big white-walled houses, houses bigger than ours, with silk cushions and vases of mimosa and waxed oaken parquet, all of them shimmering with money. And to go with them big shining cars, cars like the one Suzanne's father had, Bentleys and Lagondas and Hispano-Suizas, whose tyres whispered of money as they purred, chauffeur-driven over bright yellow gravel into the two-car garages.

They are wonderful people, I thought, I will work hard and one day I will be like them.

Incautiously I let slip something of this to my father. He was angry, yet with a pent-up anger that meant more because he said less.

" If that's how you feel," he said, " I'm sorry for you because you'll never be happy until you change your mind. Don't you see that money can't *buy* happiness ? It's something that's inside you."

I scorned to answer for I had found a friend. A rich friend my father disliked for it was that same Mr. Crombie who had called in one of his gardeners to tell him the names of his own roses. But Mr. Crombie had nine acres of garden with hothouses and asparagus beds and a staff of servants and a car that shone like a sunrise. They said in the village that he would have grudged a sparrow the crumbs from his breakfast table but I couldn't countenance that. I was too intoxicated by the smell of his money.

It was a smell I cannot describe, that seemed to hang about him as he walked, a mingled smell of good cloth and Russian leather and cigars and the hothouse carnation in his buttonhole.

Despite his riches, he walked to the railway station every day, rain or shine, for he said it was a wicked waste of petrol and the chauffeur's time and a man stayed healthier and lived longer by using the legs God had given him. As neat and well groomed as a mole, he was, with darting brown eyes behind horn-rimmed spectacles, always with a neatly furled silk umbrella as befitted a man who was in a very big line of business in the City of London.

We met every morning as I walked to the station, for Waterton House School was half an hour by train on the way to London, in a great smoky town full of red brick and factory towers. If I was late down the road he would even linger for me a minute or two.

Why should he have sought out the company of an eight-year-old? I never knew. Deep down inside I liked to think that it was because he saw in me himself as he had been half a century before—a lad with the world at his feet.

And secretly I tried with all my might to stifle the lurking belief that he talked to me because of a love of his own voice and that a gatepost that had the power to nod now and then would have done as well, and that to have lived in the same house as he, riches or no, would have been a living death inside a walnut-panelled, silk-lined coffin.

" Well, now, young man ? " he always asked, a voice that came from his nose with something of a sneer in it, " are you studying? Studying hard, now? That's what I like to hear. Never too early to have an eye on the commercial future."

But the way he talked about his beginnings as an office boy at five shillings a week in a City counting house made me think a bit. He had started with nothing, much less than I would start with, yet he was a power in the land.

"Of course I studied," he would admit. "Long hours of midnight oil, I am not ashamed to confess. Book-keeping . . . accounting . . . I made myself master of the business. The same could be done to-day. Tremendous prospects still for youngsters with sound ideas."

The longer I knew him the harder I found it to keep a sense of proportion. There was some unholy fascination about the dried-up immaculate little man with his finicky gait and his pompous talk that made you want to reach out and touch him, for to touch him would be like touching Croesus himself. And after all he was "Thomas," the mythical schoolboy, in the living flesh—"Thomas," who appeared month after month in the Careers Section of the Waterton House School Magazine. There seemed no other career deemed suitable for us then but to try and follow in Thomas's footsteps.

You see, I still remember the Saga of Thomas; he seemed to symbolise the values of the world around us. Thomas began by collecting conkers but soon exchanged them with another youngster for a pen-knife. The pen-knife he bartered for a fountain pen, which he sold for three shillings. With his three shillings Thomas purchased a stamp album from another lad then extracted all the stamps, to sell them one by one at a profit. By the time he left school he was worth so much money that he set up in business on his own. By showing "sound commercial instinct," the article told us, he was able to die a millionaire.

And Mr. Crombie, though by no means a millionaire, was a horse from the same stable. Nobody would laugh at *him*. Nobody would look through *him* as if he weren't there.

So far as my father was concerned I could walk to the station with whom I liked. But when it came to having Mr. Crombie's opinions thrust down his throat along with his bacon and tomatoes he drew the line.

"It'll help you to be a writer to study men like Crombie," he said one morning. "Nothing more."

But I wasn't so sure. "Don't know if I ever will be a writer," I said. "I thought I might go with Uncle Gilbert."

My mother was ladling the cream on to the breakfast porridge for she was always one to send her menfolk out to face the world with a good breakfast. But even she was shaken out of her habitual serenity.

"What on earth's got into you?" she said. "You'd be bored stiff within a week."

Uncle Gilbert was my father's brother, a brother who had got on so splendidly that he bought new chains of grocery stores as most men stock up on boot laces. He lived in dark Edwardian service chambers in Jermyn Street, London, and he and my father did not see eye to eye on many things.

"I could learn," I said, "and then I might be a partner one day."

My father sliced into fried gammon with force. "This is Crombie again," he said. "It's becoming insidious. Look, if you feel the call to merge grocery stores, merge grocery stores by all means. But you're more cut out for the professions from what I can see. If you don't want to write why not the Bar or the Church?"

"Mr. Crombie says they're just for those who'd never make a go in the City," I said. It was out before I could help it.

My father set his lips. "Look, there's one thing I'm not going to tolerate in this house and that is being harangued at the breakfast table by an argumentative eight-year-old. Eat your breakfast and from now on speak when you're spoken to."

"Don't want any breakfast," I said. "Not hungry."

The lie almost withered my tongue for it was kidneys and sausages and potatoes simmered golden brown in the dripping and if there was one of my mother's breakfasts that I loved, it was young lamb's kidneys just turned in the pan until they were rose-pink inside with good pork sausage from the farm, lightly grilled so that the sausage meat glistened like dew when you sliced into it. A silly obstinate mule, that was me, leaving a good breakfast untasted.

My father was unsympathetic for he had a hint of what was brewing. "He must be sickening for something," he said. "A dose of syrup of figs will put him right. But if he's sickening because I've told him the truth, he can put it in his pipe and smoke it."

I wasn't of the mettle of which hunger-strikers are made, for even with a good school lunch I had to give in and eat a good tea when I got home that day. But my stupid pride was still wounded for when my father came to say good night to me later I pretended to be asleep. He was so quiet watching me then that I thought he had gone away.

So when he suddenly said, "I know you're awake, old chap. Don't you want to say good night?" I nearly jumped a foot and gave myself away.

"Good night, Dad," I said, feeling uncomfortable now.

"Just one thing," my father said, "don't go to sleep feeling bitter. You know, Bacon said once 'Let not the sun go down upon your anger,' and it wasn't a bad maxim."

Secretly I thought it was a good one and I have always tried never to go to bed leaving a quarrel hanging in the air. So I didn't go to sleep feeling angry with my father, who I always believed was one of the best men who ever lived. But it was as if a kind of devil was in me then for I didn't stop walking with Mr. Crombie to the station or even waiting for him if I was earlier than he.

Of course, I never actually travelled on the train with him because he went straight to that section of the platform where the first-class travellers stood, to be greeted with deference even by the little knot of men almost as rich as he. Then they would all move closer together and talk in low tones, glancing over their shoulders now and then, as if they were planning a surprise take-over bid for the station and platform that very minute. And I moved on to join the other boys, covered, as I thought, with reflected glory.

One thing I noticed often enough about Mr. Crombie was that he gave advice to everyone on everything. Not only to me on how I must work hard and " show acumen " like " Thomas," but to his friends on the platform on how they might have chosen a better make of car or got better results with their roses—always standing with his feet wide apart, hands clasping the rolled umbrella behind his back, bending a little at the knees and advising them in that slightly bantering tone with the thin smile on his face.

But he would give others instructions, too, and this worried me because it wasn't in the tone that my father had taught me to speak to our servants or to any servant at all. On the way to the station he would sometimes pull up one of the men hedging and ditching for the council and tell them how they were going about it wrongly and if they tried to talk back his voice got a nasty edge on it like a saw going into metal.

Or he might reprove one of the errand boys just for whistling too loudly or caution Mr. Sparrow, the butcher, for sluicing out his shop when people were walking past and every time there would be that edge in his voice if people didn't jump to change things fast enough. But nearly always they did, for his power was in his money and money meant a lot in our world then.

Until the new garage and service depot was built inside the railway station yard Mr. Crombie was the unchallenged king of our little community.

It was always a peaceful sight on a summer morning in those days to see the gentlemen going to the City : bowler hats, stiff white collars, black coats and pin-stripe trousers, complete with spats, buttonholes and neatly-folded umbrellas. Most of them carrying *The Times* or the *Daily Telegraph*, for Mr. Fisher, our newsagent, had little call for any other papers.

As they crossed the gravelled yard the big cars would be weaving past them to the little railway station, built in red brick in King Edward's time and for some reason decorated with spires and turrets like a mosque, with the birch woods all blue and misty surrounding it and the flowerbeds on the platform a riot of lupins and pansies and rambler roses. Our station took first prize year after year for those, for only two trains an hour went through and the stationmaster and his staff had little else to do. Why, you still had a pony and trap meeting some of the trains well after I was born.

But those days were passing, which was why the service station had come for the cars and taxis, and from the first Mr. Crombie had his knife into it because he said the yard was "reverting to primitive chaos" with the cars getting petrol and everything.

He went on like this for about a year, grumbling but doing nothing, until that summer morning when we came along and there was a Ford Model A that had broken down outside the garage, right across the ramp that led into the station yard.

The cars were easing by it as best they could and the people on foot squeezing through here and there so that although there was a little confusion there wasn't chaos. But when Mr. Crombie saw it he seemed to go suddenly mad.

Until then we had been walking side by side, him mincing along and laying down the law, me with my satchel soberly slung as befitted a man who knew about mergers. But now Mr. Crombie had left me and was running—running like the wind and shouting too. And my heart sank. He was going to make a scene.

Right up to that car he ran and his gloved hand closed round the old-fashioned bulb horn. He squeezed and squeezed, seeming beside himself, the braying of the horn so loud that people were just stopping to stare and a few starting to laugh. And in between blasts of the horn he was shouting to no one in particular: "Whose car is this, then? I say, whose car is this?"

A hectic flush had come to his sallow cheeks and suddenly, I don't know why, I thought of Frankie in Form I at St. Hilda's pounding his fat fists on the desk in sheer unavailing rage. A spoilt child, whose wants were not receiving immediate attention.

But in this case, sure enough, they were. Other cars were piling up at the entrance, sounding their horns because with

Mr. Crombie in the way they couldn't get through, and suddenly
a man came out of the garage at a run and made straight for him.
A great broad-shouldered bear of a man, he was, topping six
feet—Len Turrell, a friend of Lucy's, and often about the village.

He was civil enough, though as firm as iron, as he took
Mr. Crombie by the arm and said, " Leave it now, sir. Leave it
if you wouldn't mind."

So like a firm schoolmaster dealing with a boy grown
fractious that I was reminded of Frankie more than ever. Yet
you could feel the patience beginning to go just below the
surface and you guessed the cane would be out of the cupboard
in no time at all.

Plainly Mr. Crombie was not listening to reason because he
just kept up that high-pitched shouting : " Whose car is this ?
I say, whose car is this ? " But despite that and all the comments
of the crowd and the tooting of horns and the laughter I was
close enough to hear Len Turrell say quite reasonably : " Look,
sir, the car's broken down. We're going to tow it into the yard
as soon as we're able. Just don't try and make any trouble over
it and everything will be all right."

But for all the notice that Mr. Crombie took he might never
have heard Len at all, except now he changed his tone and
began shouting : " Get this car moved ! Get it moved at once,
I say ! Get it moved ! " The whole village was his estate, you
see, in his own eyes and the car blocking the way offended him as
much as a leaf out of place on one of his shaven lawns. So as he
wouldn't move and kept sounding the horn for dear life Len
Turrell moved him.

He lifted him up, bodily, set him down a good two feet away
from the car and turning his back on him started to walk away.
And a guffaw went up from the crowd who were watching.

Suddenly Mr. Crombie ran after Len Turrell. He caught
him up just as he entered the garage, pounding him on the back
with his gloved hands like a man trying to break down a door.
And I felt sick and ashamed for near me one of Mr. Crombie's
own cronies was literally weeping with laughter at the sight.
Such a loss of control is contemptible in a child's eyes for if a

grown-up loses his dignity and calm, to a child he loses everything.

Len Turrell turned and he looked at Mr. Crombie. Not angrily, not with hatred, but with perplexity—like a big dog that turns round to find a bluebottle has alighted on his tail.

But plainly something had to be done, so quicker than a dog can snap Len had shot out his great arms and turned Mr. Crombie round very squarely facing the opposite way. And with that he lifted him. One hand holding firmly on to the collar of Mr. Crombie's blue Melton overcoat and the other clutching just as firmly to the seat of his pin-striped pants. And so holding him Len Turrell frog-marched Mr. Crombie all the way across the station yard to the very door of the station with car horns braying and a crowd a hundred strong marching behind.

When Len set him down, right in the middle of that gaping throng, I felt sorry for Mr. Crombie, even in the midst of contempt. His hat was tilted forward over his eyes and his tie had come adrift from his high starched collar. He was red in the face, simply blubbering with mindless rage and hate, though behind the whimpering sounds you could hear the spittle grating in his throat as he strove for speech.

Yet I was ashamed, too, that once I had felt that about wanting to touch him, for shorn of his boardroom manner and people eager to lick his boots he was as pitiful and insignificant as a gnat drowning in a puddle.

"Sue," he screamed in a thin reedy voice, his eyes darting, "I'll sue . . . that's what . . . cost *you* your job . . . have the coat off your back."

"If it comes to suing," said Len Turrell, quite easy in his conscience, "it was you what struck the first blow, sir. That and trespassing on my property. So it's up to you." And there was a growl of approval from all the men standing round in their City suits, watching.

"Oh," cried Mr. Crombie, lips wet and shining. "Oh. Oh. Oh!" He stamped his little feet in rage then, for the crowd was laughing again but contemptuously now and pushing past to the platform. And though I despised him more than ever I had sought him as a friend for better or worse, so I made a way through the crowd. And I said: " Sir . . . Mr. Crombie . . . can I help dust you down ? "

Imagine the shock I had when he turned on me. "Get away," he shouted, " take your hands away from me . . . grinning fool of a boy . . . get away."

And with that he stumbled almost weeping into the station, but my belief is that he hid in the lavatory until the train had gone and then went home again.

What I do know is that he never sued Len Turrell and that in some indefinable way the real awe people felt for him had gone from that day on. He never waited for me again and by nightfall the story was all over the village. The first thing my father said when he came in that night, eyes twinkling, was, " Well, I hear a friend of yours got himself into a little trouble to-day."

" Yes," I said, busy with French verbs and not anxious to talk about it. For I saw it as my shame as much as Mr. Crombie's.

My father's hand came on my shoulder. " Well," he said, " I thought you'd find it wasn't worth it. And I know you have, so now we'll forget it. Now, my dear," for just then my mother had come into the room, " what have we got for dinner to-night? "

" I thought perhaps a mushroom omelet," my mother said. " Sparrow did send some pork chops up by mistake, they should have gone to the Crombies, from the name on the bill. But I suppose you'd find them too rich so I can send them back."

" No," my father said, with surprising firmness. " No. I could eat a pork chop for dinner to-night and some fresh sage and onion stuffing too. And hang them being too rich. That's something to worry about in men, not pork chops."

And he strolled upstairs to wash his hands, whistling as he went.

CHAPTER EIGHT

THE WAY WE LIVED THEN

When I was a boy with never a crack in my heart

W. B. YEATS

How DID we live then? I must confess we lived very well in those years when the foundations of our world were cracking secretly underfoot like concrete when the frost has flawed it.

On that same station platform where Mr. Crombie was put to shame I, a young onlooker with a satchelful of books and a pocketful of marbles, heard the fate of the world settled a score of times. Weary men, cynical men, hopeful men, in stiff collars and formal cutaways sweated at Geneva, wrote notes in Chancellories, talked of disarmament but in our little world, Heaven forgive us, it was simpler. " This fellow Hitler," said Mr. Graveney, the bank manager, rustling his *Daily Telegraph* angrily one summer morning, " is behaving like a jackanapes." And my father, on the station platform beside him, scanning his *Times* for some sign of reassurance agreed tight-lipped. " His conduct is un-English." At the height of that era you could utter no greater condemnation.

Our anxieties had lain closer to the hearth—from the crystal set with its clamping earphones (" 2LO calling ") bought especially to hear the King on Christmas Day, to one of the first and shiniest Marconi radios ever to be accepted in the district. Fired by the prospect of hearing Wimbledon week direct, of following the fortunes of Tilden and Helen Wills Moody set by set, my father took the plunge and broke our privacy and linked us by way of the National Programme to the outside world. " And can you," an awed neighbour asked him, " hear the *ping* of the ball ? "

Yes, you could hear the ping of the ball and many other things besides : Henry Hall's dance orchestra, the cheerful idiocies of Clapham and Dwyer, the Children's Hour with Larry the Lamb, Christopher Stone and his gramophone records. But our listening time was as carefully rationed as a dose of physic, and it was the old victrola, wound by hand, that still had pride of place, perhaps with Master Ernest Lush singing " Oh for the Wings of a Dove." The depression was on, we were " off " the Gold Standard, people as my father put it, were " hard up." But there was no sign of it on the face of our world. We wound the victrola and banished depression with " There's a Good Time Coming " and " Who's Afraid of the Big Bad Wolf ? " We were determined, as my father said, not to become " slaves of a wooden box that made sounds."

After all we needed time to read : the hall table was always piled with books just arrived from Boots' Library or just going back—*The Bridge of San Luis Rey*, *The Story of San Michele*, *Anthony Adverse*. Time to go to the cinema and see Ronald Coleman and Greta Garbo though all the grown-ups agreed with my father that the talkies " would never take." Time for the tennis-parties of those days, when my father not only mowed every inch of the grass court by hand, trusting no gardener's skill, but mixed his own whiting and marked the court and adjusted his own net. Oh, the mounds of cucumber sandwiches that Lucy cut on those golden Saturday afternoons, the pints of tea she brewed, the hams and glazed tongues she sliced for late supper, the brimming jugs of cider. What a whitening of tennis-shoes and an unpressing of rackets and an ironing of knife-edged creases into white flannels. To see the striped deck-chairs ranged in a long cool row under the maples, to hear the cries of " Sorry partner " and " Love-forty " you would not have guessed our world lay in peril.

You would not have guessed it then, and only rarely at other times. Not from the things the grown-ups talked about in tones as conscious of the right opinion held as those political discussions on the station platform—the Culbertson system, the iniquity of body-line bowling, the importance of vitamins and cod-liver oil when you brought up children, the unashamed decadence of a generation that could tolerate crooners. These were the things talked about in the years when my mother wore floppy sun hats and the village bazaar with its White Elephant stalls and its loudspeakers lilting Edward German was the greatest event of the week, the kind of bazaar at which I once disgraced myself for ever by spitting out the contents of my first mustard-and-cress sandwich with a roar of " Wozzis—grass ? "

Dear enduring days, we believed you would endure for ever, as solid as the gilt-edged securities that gave foundation to our faith. Always and for ever the same, like the old good Christmases when a fir tree twelve feet high darkened the main hall and the house thrilled to the secret rustle of aunts wrapping brown paper parcels and at our door on Christmas Eve little boys with frost-pinched fingers sang " The First Noel." As unchanging as the crackers, the games of charades, the magic moment when the lights went out and we scorched our fingers dipping for raisins in a blue flickering lake of flaming brandy. As sure and charted as a carving knife whittling the white breast of an eighteen-pound turkey, with a pudding full of sixpences to follow.

We were so right then. We were so sure. God had blessed us and our world as gravely and eternally as the old King gave us all his blessing in his broadcast address each Christmas afternoon. And in our pride and our blindness we decreed to the years the harvest that they should yield us.

.   .   .

If I was happier now that the thrall of Mr. Crombie was broken, I still lacked a friend older than my years. Friendships in school I had in plenty but if a boy is to become a man there are times when he needs a man for his friend, a man other than his father.

But for this I had to wait a little though not too long.

Meanwhile I was happy at Waterton House and it is good to look back now on the life of a preparatory school of those days. A great gloomy-looking, yellow-brick building it was, shut off from the main road by a low brick wall and a stony plot of starved front garden. I think nothing would ever have grown in that garden, for all day the factory chimneys stained the crystal sky with soot so that contented as I was at school I was always happiest to take the train out of town, back to the green freshness of our garden.

Indeed it has been the same all my life, for visits to London with my mother in the school holidays to buy a new blazer or grey flannel shorts at Daniel Neal's and eat pink ices at Gunter's, or to see one of the dozen or more shows they staged for children then—*Treasure Island*, perhaps, or *Alice Through the Looking Glass* —well, th y palled as quickly as a surfeit of chocolate milk shakes. In the City I liked it best with my father, exploring the Tower of London and old churches behind St. Paul's on Saturday afternoons so quiet you could hear a tug cry all the way from Limehouse Reach.

But back to school now.

If it was dark outside it was dark enough inside too, but a comfortable darkness that some of the old Victorian houses had, a darkness that smelt of old plimsolls and polished linoleum and leaking gas and at times of the beef stew and boiled cabbage that came floating up from the basement kitchen. There were even parts of the school still lit by gas and in the basement that housed our boot lockers, where the black beetles scurried on the stone floor, you could have believed you were living between the pages of a Victorian novel.

But there was nothing gloomy or Victorian about the way they treated us, so if ever I needed proof that it is the people you live with who matter most I had it there.

Mr. and Mrs. Chailey, who owned the school, must have been well into their sixties, for they had been forty years married and brought up children of their own and that was the way they ran things all the years I was there—as a big jolly family party where you had to mind your manners and the cane was not unknown, but where you learnt to take a joke as easily as crack one. At lunch-time when we all crowded on to benches round a long table in the ground floor dining-room there was old Mr. Chailey at one end of the table, carving the roast or ladling out the stew, and looking with his high white collar, his black Master of Arts gown and his ragged white moustache just like Mr. Lloyd George in the newsreel pictures. And at the other end, serving up the vegetables and potatoes and gravy and later the treacle pudding would be Mrs. Chailey, a great jolly mountain of a woman, who still wore a high-necked dress that swept her ankles with a cameo brooch pinned into place and her hair piled high in the style of King Edward's time.

No endless games of " Coffee-pots " or polite toying with meagre helpings here. Instead, with fifty or more boys chattering like magpies on a branch and the masters packed in amongst us, it was like feeding time in a select private zoo :

" Sir ! Sir ! I say, sir . . ."

" Shut *up*, Collier. Can't you see I'm talking to Jones ? "

" No, but, *sir*—are we going to lick Mercer's at soccer next week ? "

" How do I know, you chump ? That's up to you and the rest of the team, isn't it ? "

" Sir . . ."

" *Sir*. . . ."

Mrs. Chailey's turn now, merry grey eyes sparkling, plump pink cheeks pouting with pretended annoyance : " Boys, boys, don't be so aggravating . . . I can't even make Mr. Chailey hear . . . George, see that Nicolson has another helping of stew . . . he'll be useless in goal if he doesn't get a bit more beef on him . . ."

"Mm ? What ? Oh . . . by all means . . . growing boy . . . most important thing . . . nourishment . . ." That was old Mr. Chailey at any time. He grunted the linking words in sentences ; few verbs, no prepositions.

" Sir . . ."

" *Sir* . . ."

"Hey, Jackson, did you see this week's *Magnet*? There's an absolutely peachy story in it . . ."

"Jones, what extraordinary language is that?" Mrs. Chailey was in the lists again. "*Peachy*? I have no idea what you mean? What's that when it's at home?"

"Well . . . it means super, really, Mrs. Chailey . . ."

Everything was "peachy" then or "super."

In the background was old Mr. Chailey, grumbling away in a monotone about Lord Roberts with whom he had served in the Boer War: "Hm . . . 'Bobs' . . . yes, that's it . . . called him 'Bobs' . . . 'fore your time, of course . . . weren't thought of then . . . 'fore your father's time, if it comes to that . . . grandfather's time, right enough though . . . remembered him well . . . 'Bobs' . . ."

No grumbles about second helpings or even thirds. An endless stream of plates passing to and fro, fro and to, with Mrs. Chailey's voice, brisk and coaxing above the clatter of china :

"Come on, Jackson, you can manage some more rice pudding . . . you'll make more sense of those fractions then . . . Collier, you've had four helpings, you'll bust, boy . . . Jones, you've cut your knee . . . if I thought you'd been fighting I should ask Mr. Chailey to dust your britches . . , I suppose you fell down . . . don't answer or you may make me angry . . . come to the study after lunch and I'll dress it for you . . . now come along, boys, pass those plates and don't aggravate . . . Collier, you'd had *enough*, how many more times, boy . . ."

"Sir . . ."

"*Sir*. . . ."

Strictly speaking we were not supposed to fight in school hours. We could be caned for it, and that made sense for in those dark cramped corridors and classrooms we might have done ourselves much damage. But Mr. and Mrs. Chailey, who had brought up children of their own, had found a way round that. They brought in lunch-time walks for the sake of exercise with one of the younger, tougher masters like Mr. Vereker, the scoutmaster, in charge of the crocodile. His instructions were to take us where we could " let off steam," which meant some fields ten minutes' walk away. Once there, Mr. Vereker dismissed us with a brisk " Go to it, chaps," sat on a log, lit his pipe and turned his back on us. And there we climbed trees, fought epic battles for the possession of a log or the bank of a stream and cut and bruised ourselves as gloriously as any boy has a right to.

But each day when we returned for lunch the same fiction prevailed. As Mr. Vereker, poker-faced, mustered us to change our shoes in the locker room, Mrs. Chailey bubbled at the head of the basement stairs—magnificent, motherly, mountainous.

" Ah, Mr. Vereker, so you're back . . . and the boys enjoyed themselves, I suppose ? . . . it was a good walk ? . . . Good lord alive, Jackson, what have you done to your eye ? . . . *knocked* it against a tree ? . . . Mr. Vereker, they surely haven't been fighting ? . . . well, if that's the story and you're all sticking to it . . . that's what you say nowadays, isn't it ? . . . Jackson, go and knock at the kitchen door, ask Millie for some beefsteak with the blood in it . . . goodness, how boys do aggravate. . . ."

I have heard it said that boys are cruel in the mass but it was not so at Waterton House. You could have numbered the boys who were like that on the fingers of one hand, and saved a finger or two even then.

In such a small community we knew our masters well, their failings as well as the good that was in them, but I never once saw anyone try to take advantage of them or to make a cruel joke at their expense. Young Mr. Lea, with the bright feverish eyes and the skin as transparent as a flower petal, had the face of a sick angel; often he bent double over his desk, coughing and coughing into a clean, white handkerchief, but when at last he straightened up the white linen held the tinge of scarlet silk.

Sometimes the coughing became so bad that Mr. Lea had to go home early, but furtively down the back path, like one of us playing truant. He did not want Mr. and Mrs. Chailey to

know he had gone. He did not want them to know that he
coughed at all.

One outburst of noise from the unattended classroom then
and his secret might have been out for good and all. But at those
times we were as quiet as young birds after nightfall, so that I
think the Chaileys never knew.

They had no notion either that Mr. Kerridge's eyes were
failing so that he tumbled over chairs and couldn't find the place
in Hall and Knight's Algebra without help, because if ever Mr.
Chailey dropped in to see how a lesson was going there was
always a boy or two willing to move the blackboard or even, as
never happened at other times, to stand up and answer questions.
The important thing was to act as a decoy to prevent Mr. Chailey
seeing that Mr. Kerridge was talking in his direction without
really focusing him at all.

Mind you, I think the Chaileys knew when to let well alone,
for they could afford to pay their staff little enough and though
most of the masters had their Bachelor of Arts degree not one
had been able to afford the extra fees at university that would have
made them Masters of Arts. We all knew that Mr. Maurice,
the deputy headmaster, besides being a bit of a showman, was
fond of the bottle, too. With his handsome lined face and his
double-breasted suits he played lead year after year when the local
operatic society put on *Monsieur Beaucaire* or *The Desert Song* but
on the days he lunched out of school he came back as often
as not with his cheeks the colour of good grilling steak to
doze away the afternoon.

But just as with Mr. Lea, we continued to amuse ourselves
tactfully without so much noise as would have forced Mr. Chailey
to investigate.

For it was only once in a while that such little crises arose
and if the world at large would have called these men failures
we measured them by what they gave to us. If Mr. Maurice was
sometimes fuddled, there were other times when his brain was
needle-sharp and he laboured to make ours the same—so that a
boy might find himself on his feet bidden to address the class
on the subject that most interested *him* with the rest of us firing

questions right and left. There was many a boy written off as a blockhead who discovered his true self on his feet in Mr. Maurice's classroom revealing with glowing cheeks that to him the one real urgent thing in life was keeping tropical fish or growing mushrooms.

We learned a lot about enthusiasm in Mr. Maurice's class and with Mr. Lea, too, because he had a gift for seeing the past as if in a crystal, and in bringing it vividly to life. And sometimes when we were all bored stiff with Tudor dates and Henry VIII's battles with the Pope, Mr. Lea would wipe his eyes after a fit of coughing and say: " Look, try and see it, chaps . . . even in quite good houses, you know, there were rushes covering the floor, thick layers of them, with all the filth and the beef bones dropping among them and rats nesting there so if you wanted the place cleaner you just put down a fresh lot of rushes . . . and the meat, you know, that was often green so they'd coat it in sugar and pickle . . . anything to cover up the taste . . ."

And at times like that we would be four hundred years back from that hot little classroom with its yellow pitch-pine desks, smelling of dust and ink and the wood pigeons scolding in the chestnut trees outside, sharing the stink and the savagery and the colour of an age we had never known.

But if those days were good and the friendships good, too, the greatest friendship was not with a boy at all, and the way it began was strange.

.   .   .

It was a Sunday in November, I recall, an iron day of black frost. The year was 1933. That morning the house was stirring early with a light showing in every room by seven and the clatter of plates and roasting tins enough to bring on a headache by ten. No three hours in the bath for my father that morning, for some of his family were coming to spend the day and there would be nine of us all told.

So an extra leaf must be inserted in the dining-room table and the fires lit early and all the silver and the wine glasses polished yet again and there was Lucy and her friend, pretty little Mrs. May (who originally came to help for three weeks but stayed thirty years and is my good and trusted friend still) washing every plate and sauce-boat and tureen and vegetable dish of a forty-piece service ready for the feast.

There was my mother, outwardly calm but inwardly on pins with a thousand things on her mind, looking to see that the stuffing for the chicken was moist enough and that there were enough cloves in the bread sauce while Mr. May, who had succeeded Lucy's father, delivered wooden trays of freshly-picked brussels sprouts and potatoes from the clamp at the kitchen door. But no matter how many he delivered it was never enough for what with the light and the steam and the steady hissing and sizzling from the oven the kitchen seemed like one great yawning mouth that would seize upon everything eatable and roast it or boil it or beat it into a smooth creamy sauce.

As for my father he was as full of zest as I have ever seen him as he decanted sherry and whisky and struggled with flagons of beer and high-necked golden bottles of wine; for if there was one thing that sent his spirits soaring it was to have his family about him.

All the memories of his South London boyhood crowded back on him then and he was ready to argue until midnight about all the great abstractions they had wrangled over since time began.

By twelve o'clock, when the kitchen was as full of steam as a Turkish bath, so that my mother and Lucy and Mrs. May had no heart to do more than exchange glances, and a merry fire was blazing in the sitting-room grate, they all arrived in the old Daimler hire-car that the local garage had run since 1919. And it was then that I really took in my Uncle Victor for the first time.

Of course I had heard all about his famous fight with the Covent Garden porter and about his careers as a lawyer and an actor and a novelist and an inventor and a market-gardener and I had seen him at least once before. A strange weather-beaten old man he had seemed then, in a well-cut if rumpled suit

116

of pepper-and-salt tweeds, wearing steel spectacles and a tweed fishing hat which he forgot to remove until reminded.

All day he had crouched forward on his chair like a man riding a motor-cycle, fierce blue eyes glaring from beneath bushy brows, talking with the enthusiasm of a man forty years his junior and trumpeting like a rogue elephant if anyone disagreed with him. That day he had missed his last train and we had to put him up for the night.

This Sunday we had thought it might be the same for no amount of company deterred my Uncle Victor. Not my Aunt Kate nor my Uncle William Henry, of course, because they and Aunt Helen Victoria lived with Uncle Victor, unmarried Colliers every one, in a cottage four miles away where they had just moved to be near my father. Aunt Emily, who was married, was a brisk little woman who spoke of herself as " a breath of real fresh air," but she was Uncle Victor's sister and so not much problem either.

But Uncle Hubert, her husband, a power in the insurance world, whom we had not seen for years, might have chilled the stoutest heart.

He was a tall thin man, stooped and melancholy, with an undertaker's lack-lustre eye and a nose that was always in frosty weather adorned with a dewdrop. He divided all human nature into two categories, good risks and bad risks, and his hobby was analysing the death rates among the wealthier citizens listed in *The Times* in relation to the money they left. Since we had last seen him he had done increasingly well in life and it soon became plain that he expected us to pay tribute to this. Our tribute would be to listen while Uncle Hubert talked.

Now Uncle Victor and Uncle Hubert had not met for ten years but my Uncle Victor, as I heard it from my father, had never forgiven Uncle Hubert for referring to him, during his career as a novelist, as " that no-good scribbling fellow."

But whether even Uncle Victor, smarting under this old slight, could prevail against him seemed doubtful. For my Uncle Hubert was a man of weighty words, with a surprisingly deep voice for such a thin man, whose sentences rolled ponderously, one from the other, on and on, like skittles down a bowling alley.

He had been talking like this for half an hour before we went into lunch, warming his rump at the drawing-room fire. All the time I could see my father sinking deeper and deeper into gloom. There was going to be none of the fire of the old days. There would be no arguments. Only Uncle William Henry murmured an occasional " Very true, old friend " but Uncle Victor seemed withdrawn, thoughtful, like a professor pondering a thesis.

Sometimes he muttered "Ha" or "Hmm" but it was obvious he was no match for Uncle Hubert and that his sixty-five years were telling on him.

Even the sight of my father carving the chickens, all pink and golden brown on a big blue willow-pattern dish didn't lessen my dismay. We were in for one of the dullest days on record.

". . . a complicated system of commerce, of course," Uncle Hubert was saying, "complicated but efficient. Strangely enough I myself at that time was acting. . . ."

That started it.

" *Acting*," roared Uncle Victor suddenly, so loudly that my mother almost dropped a dish of sausages. " What do half of them know about acting anyway ? In the old fit-up theatres, *yes*—there a man learned to act ! But drawing-room comedies, mincing about with cups of tea, passing bon-bons—*flummery !* "

Even at normal pitch Uncle Victor's voice was like a ship's captain's using a loud-hailer in a fog. Lucy and Mrs. May, eating lunch in the kitchen, must have thought a fight had broken out.

" Not *that* sort of acting," said Uncle Hubert irritably, his chicken cooling before him. " I was acting manager . . ."

Uncle Victor beamed. He was warming to this argument. But he was not letting his chicken get cold. He waved a big steaming forkful amiably at Uncle Hubert.

" Actor-managers," he bellowed, " were all very well. But no man can play *Hamlet* and tunes on a cash register at the same time. Can he now ? "

"That's beside the point," Uncle Hubert fumed. "What I meant . . ."

"Not beside the point at all," Uncle Victor shouted. "The point is, can he or can't he ? And speak up—I'm a bit deaf to-day —I think it's this east wind."

"All right, then," bawled Uncle Hubert, furiously. "He can't." And with that disposed of he was ready once more to take up the thread of his discourse.

But the opportunity was lost. My mother was reminding him that his lunch was getting cold. And as if that wasn't bad enough Uncle Victor had the attention of the rest of the company, explaining how an actor-manager he had worked with on a tour of the Outer Hebrides had had his big scene in *A Woman Wronged* ruined by having to get up off his death-bed to let down the last-act curtain, the scene-shifter having retired to the local at the time.

The conversation became general. We began to enjoy ourselves.

When the apple pie and cream came in Uncle Hubert tried again. I was busy passing plates and soft sugar as if my life depended on it when I heard : ". . . need for foresight and prudence should have been plain to any Treasury . . . but what happened ? Eating into our reserves . . ."

"If it comes to eating," said Uncle Victor suddenly, "I should say William Henry, young Charles here and myself hold the records on that. Remember breakfast at The Feathers, Ludlow, in the summer of '06 ? "

"Very well," said my father, enjoying himself for some reason or other.

Uncle Hubert, unwilling to be foiled again, tried sarcasm. "I was speaking," he said clearly and sharply, "of a very different kind of eating."

"And it *is* a different kind of eating," said Uncle Victor equably. "Present company excepted, Eveline, and a little more of the cream, if I may. But how many breakfasts do you see nowadays like the old Feathers could put on at a pinch ? And how many men could walk all night long and then eat it ? What's that, Hubert ?—I'm as deaf as a post to-day. Meant to drop in some warm oil but it clean slipped my mind."

" I'm talking about gold reserves, Victor," Uncle Hubert shouted, pounding his spoon with vexation.

" Gold reserves ? " said Uncle Victor, bland as a baby. " Well, what have they got to do with breakfast at The Feathers, Ludlow ? A pigeon pie, half a York ham, a loaf and a half of bread and three pints of coffee or I'm a Dutchman."

" Oh, hold on," my father protested, " why, even the three of us . . ."

" Well, perhaps it was two pints," Uncle Victor conceded. " Memory plays tricks. It was a pigeon pie—crust and all. Well, yes, Eveline, if you press me I think I will. . . ."

He kept this up for much of the afternoon. No sooner did Uncle Hubert raise a subject than Uncle Victor, growing rapidly deafer, took him up on some chance phrase and in no time at all they were talking at cross-purposes about something different. Finally, about three o'clock, Uncle Hubert in desperation proposed a walk—what he called " a short constitutional."

The women decided to stay by the fire and gossip and my father pleaded business with a bonfire. So, muffled up against the greying afternoon, we set out—Uncle Hubert, Uncle William Henry, Uncle Victor and myself.

Uncle Hubert and Uncle William Henry set out in front with us bringing up the rear. The two uncles walked gravely, heads bent, hands clasped behind their backs, like elder statesmen in conference. Uncle Victor had a brisk swinging stride as befitted a man in his sixties who still often walked thirty miles a day for sheer pleasure. Soon we had passed them.

Without saying anything, I think the sight of Uncle Hubert's bowler hat was irking us. It was tall and conical and, perched on the very tip of his head, it made him look more like an undertaker than ever.

Mindful of Uncle Victor's deafness I began to pipe up as loudly as I could. " No need to shout, old son," said Uncle Victor amiably, " I can hear you." Though the light was fading

I had the impression that he winked. " Some people you can hear better than others."

And as we walked, trudging side by side through the black afternoon, he began to talk—about that breakfast at The Feathers, Ludlow, about acting in fit-up theatres when they were so poor they had to sleep on the stage, about his own boyhood and the games they had played. " Catapulting now . . . why, we could bowl over a rabbit on the run clean as a whistle at fifteen yards."

" I have a catapult," I said shyly. " Here." It was a shiny aluminium one with a brand-new rubber sling and I was fiercely proud of it.

" H'm." To see his lips purse so dubiously my heart sank. " My son, that's no more use to you than a sausage machine. A fork like that's got no ' whip.' Good stout ash, that's what you want, with a nice short handle. Still . . ." Strangely wistful he looked all of a sudden and moistening his lips . . . " let's see you try it."

We were on the homeward road now, which bordered the farm's five-acre field. The uncles were out of sight somewhere behind. Somehow I couldn't see either of them scrambling over a wire fence to practise catapult shots in a field on a November afternoon. But it seemed natural enough to Uncle Victor.

We collected pebbles, the best we could—though small ones smoothed in stream beds made the best ammunition, said Uncle Victor—and I tried to knock over a tin can that we had found from ten yards away. But it was useless. I failed time and again.

" The light's no good," I said.

" *Light !* " shouted Uncle Victor so loudly that I quaked. " It's *you* that's no good, not the light. Holding the catapult level with your eyes and hauling on the sling like a stevedore— why, the boy's as slow as a toad."

Now he grabbed the catapult from me. I had the feeling he had been wanting to do this all along. " Now I'll show you, my son—and I guarantee I'll knock a hole in that can at ten yards and not even use a pebble. A catapult's got the velocity of a rifle you know, if you use it right."

" What will you use ? " I asked remorselessly.

" Why, a—a . . ." Uncle Victor sought desperately for inspiration and now his eyes lit on the pine wood that bordered the farm, perched high above the railway station ". . . well, in that wood over there I'd like to bet we'd find some very fine fir cones to serve the purpose."

Now I was almost sure he was bluffing but I was not going to let him off that easily. And if anyone could really pierce a hole in a tin can with a fir cone at ten yards I wanted to see it done.

At the double now, with the blood coming to our cheeks and our breath like a veil about our faces, pounding over the stubble. Over the wire fence and into the dark resin-smelling vault of the wood, with our boots making no sound on the pile carpet of needles. And there were fir cones, sure enough—long, heavy cylinders like small dry hand-grenades. And I was just saying " I don't see . . ." when Uncle Victor hushed me.

We could hear voices. And we could hear footsteps.

The road home ran right past the pine wood and Uncle William Henry and Uncle Hubert were within ten yards of us without knowing it. Deep and solemn came their voices, analysing the state of the world's finances, but both of us were not really listening but looking.

From where we crouched all we could see, looming larger than life itself, was that hated bowler hat of Uncle Hubert's moving slowly and inexorably across our line of vision like a bottle in a shooting-gallery.

And in that second I saw yet did not see a thousand things : the glint of sheer devilry in Uncle Victor's eyes, like the mischief incarnate in every boy that ever was, and in one single lightning flash his arm came up, three fingers holding the handle of the fork, first finger and thumb braced on the sides, and faster than a bullet the cone had gone. Next instant the bowler hat had gone too, spun away as if by a giant hand.

A great roar came from Uncle Hubert—a roar not of pain but of wounded pride.

" My hat ! I've been shot . . . some ruffian's shot off my hat ! "

Then Uncle William Henry's voice: " Don't worry, old friend . . . I've got it . . . some young boys up to their tomfoolery . . ."

" I'll give them tomfoolery," Uncle Hubert was shouting, " I'll give them a taste of my walking-stick . . . just let them wait. . . ."

But we were not waiting. We were doubling away across the fields, using the pine wood as cover, to a point a quarter of a mile away where the lane led up to our house. And the first thing Uncle Victor said, with true piety, as he got breath was : " God forgive me, I succumbed to temptation . . . I shot off old Hubert's hat."

Suddenly he began to chuckle. Presently, in between chuckles, he said : " Hubert was always a poor thing . . . and I've waited thirty years for that, ever since the day Emily married him."

He chuckled again and said : " I may have been a no-good scribbling fellow but by Christmas I know how to use a catapult."

He quickened his step. " Not a word to the others, old son —they might not understand. At this moment we have nothing weightier on our minds than tea and buttered muffins."

And through the darkening afternoon we went home together, arm in arm, in the way that old and good friends will.

CHAPTER NINE

A CHILDHOOD HERO

His heart's his mouth,
What his breast forges, that his tongue must vent

WILLIAM SHAKESPEARE
Coriolanus

" CAREFUL," MY Uncle Victor whispered, " Keep low. Someone's coming back."

I made no answer, only swallowed with my heart like a pounding engine against my ribs, shrinking deeper still into hot dry grass.

August sun dazzled raw white and blinding on the metals of the railway line but from where we lay, in head-high grass on the cutting above, we could not see the track, vanishing into blue distance between the line of hills. We could hear only the steady crunching on the gravel beside the rails as a ganger made his way back along the track to where we were lying. We had been ·lying there for an hour now and we were hot and thirsty but excited too because the gangers were looking for us.

No sabotage was in our minds but the possession of a wild flower—one single spike of blooms, the shape of bells that grew in purple drifts along the cutting not a hundred yards from where we lay. Often we had seen it from the train in passing but this morning we meant to have a sprig of it, to be identified later from one of the old dog-eared flower books that Uncle Victor kept in his study.

Wild flowers, wild birds, all manner of fish and fowl—to

search out these we had braved every imaginable danger, Uncle Victor and I, in the eight months we had been firm friends.

It was he who had taught me to tickle trout in the deep cold pool that lay near the windows of a great manor house twelve miles from my home—so that part of your mind was taken up by the pain of icy water which seems to bruise your arm to the biceps and part by the sheer skill of getting your little finger inside the old trout's gill and heaving him on to the bank and part in wondering whether a butler or a gamekeeper or my lord himself would be out of those french windows to raise the devil.

We were lucky that time for we got our trout and we lit a fire in my lord's woods and baked our fish on hot stones as Englishmen have delighted to do since Chaucer's time. But at other times we were not so lucky and the gamekeepers had put a shot or two after us the time we went to hunt for white butterfly orchids in the pheasant coverts of the Hall woods and the time we invaded the Duke's fishing preserves to watch the kingfisher's nest through field-glasses.

We did not look like being lucky this morning either. The gangers had caught only one glimpse of us on this cutting an hour back but if they did not know where we were hiding or why they were determined to find out.

An uncomfortable business that could have been, to be caught trespassing on railway property with a flimsy excuse. It might mean detention until the local bobby arrived to sort things out, perhaps a summons and a fine.

Worse, it would mean my parents knowing that the nature rambles which Uncle Victor and I took almost every day of the school holidays, winter and summer—a whole four months of the year, remember—were often fraught with peril to life and limb.

" Not a word to the others, old son," Uncle Victor often said, just as he had done over the glorious affair of Uncle Hubert's hat. " They might not understand." Now my parents might conceivably have understood about Uncle Hubert's hat. But what would they have said about the time we had clambered through the window of a slowly-moving train on to the footboard of one drawn up parallel to avoid being carried non-stop to the coast ?

Often they said that Uncle was wonderfully agile for his age but if they knew just how agile I think our walks might have ceased altogether.

Now the footsteps had died away along the railway track. Beside me there was a stealthy rustling as Uncle Victor drew from his pocket—a time-table.

" There's a train due in the station up there just after midday," he whispered. " But remember the gradient sign down the track . . . the train has to whistle then. And that's a mile away. See our chance ? "

" No," I said obtusely.

" Why, you addle-pated troglodyte," hissed Uncle Victor fiercely. " When the train whistles, the gangers'll clear the track, won't they ? They'll stand well to one side to let the train go past. There's a curve in the bank that'll screen us from view and that'll just give me time to nip along in cover, grab the plant and get back here."

" But what about me ? " I objected, " I could go."

" You stay here and keep your old eyes peeled for the other one. It's my belief he's gone up the line to report to the station. You must cover my retreat."

It seemed to me that Uncle Victor was taking on more than his due share of danger. But it made sense. The station lay only three hundred yards up the line to our right and it needed watching. The old steam train which still ran between these wild chalk hills which were our hunting ground would be coming from our left and would take a good two minutes to cover the mile that lay between us and the start of the gradient. So Uncle stood a chance.

A second passed, then we stiffened. A mile away on the hot still morning we heard the train cry.

" I'm off," Uncle Victor breathed and suddenly he had gone, snaking away through scrub and high grass in the way that only he could—head low, as flat on his belly as a grass snake, using only his elbows to propel him. He said he had learned it from a poacher and it was easy to believe him.

Minutes passed in the hot stillness. I could hear the faint far-off pulsing as the train drew nearer. At the same time I heard footsteps coming hard from the direction of the station. Round the bend in the track, red-faced and sweating in a shirt open to his waist and corduroy pants, came one of the biggest, toughest gangers I had ever seen.

At that moment, from up the track, came a wild swelling roar of triumph, such as the field will give when a fox breaks cover. The big ganger passed me at a trot, not seeing me. Unable to bear it any longer I jumped up.

And then I saw—they had Uncle Victor cornered. As tough as whipcord he was and running hard, his old fishing hat set squarely on his silver head, the purple flower clutched tightly in his grasp. But a whole line of gangers streamed after him, yelling, the distance narrowing every second. Next instant he would run full tilt into the big ganger's arms.

With a shout I dashed to the edge of the cutting, seizing a clod of earth and pitching it clean at the big man's head.

Wonder of wonders, it worked! With a snarl he swung away from Uncle Victor and began clawing his way up the crumbling chalk shelf towards me. I had not heard such interesting words since the milkman fell headlong over my scooter in the drive.

And in that minute the train came round the bend three hundred yards away and both Uncle Victor and I saw at the same moment what we must do. With a great sweep of his arm Uncle Victor signalled " Over ! "

So over it was. After all those months in his company I was as bronzed and wiry and agile as a chimpanzee and the ganger was hampered by his bulk. In one roaring white cascade of chalk I was down the cutting and on to the track with the big man marooned up on the bluff like a treed squirrel and bawling to make the heavens fall.

And now the train came on, bulking enormously, little darts of steam licking round its pistons, a great plume of smoke bannering away behind, thundering on the hot metals so close that as we darted across its path we were only feet away from the flying wheels. But we were across, Uncle Victor and I, though the hot breath of the train scorched our cheeks like a desert wind, and as coach after coach rumbled in its wake the gangers were left behind cheated of their prey.

But we were running still, along the opposite cleft of the cutting, down a twisting track carved for the railway workers, though there was one bad moment at the station level crossing when the stationmaster and one of his porters tried to bar our way. But we dodged them as easily as two-year-olds among the milk churns and the rolling stock and were away on to a country bus at the bottom of the road.

" Well, well," Uncle Victor said when we were nicely settled on the top deck and the bus was bearing us from the scene of our crime towards the nearest market town, "we must take care of this when we risked the wrath of the Philistine hordes to get it."

And he cradled the spike of purple bells very gently inside an empty tobacco tin and shut tight the lid, so that the plant would be hermetically sealed and would not wither. All over his person, in deep unexpected pockets, you found those empty tobacco tins so that a fern or a clump of moss or a wild bird's egg would find sanctuary until he had taken it home to identify.

He chuckled, " I don't know what your father would say," he said. " I'm sure, I don't."

" I do," I supplied. " He'd say ' the game's not worth the candle.' " My father liked life to run smoothly and peacefully and as much as anything the joy we got from our forays would have puzzled him.

Uncle Victor nodded sagely. " In a way, of course," he said, " your father's right. If there were more men in it like Charles it wouldn't be a bad world. It needs just a few of us, though, who'll take a risk now and again—climb a mountain just to see what's at the top, go down a pot-hole to see what's at the bottom."

He patted the tin box that held the flower. It was a Canterbury Bell, one of seven varieties that grew wild in our county, though I had not known there was more than one kind until Uncle Victor told me.

"Perhaps by to-night," he said, "we'll be famous because we've discovered a new species. Perhaps we won't. The main thing is, you know, we tried."

In the end, I think, it turned out to be one of the commonest varieties of all, but of course he was right. We had done our best. We had tried.

      .   .   .

I don't remember how we spent the rest of that day. My belief now is we bought our lunch at a little wayside pub just outside the town, a thatched whitewashed pub by an old stone bridge that ran over a clear, pebbled stream. I think we took our warm new bread, our cheese and pickled onions and pints of shandy-gaff to the shade of an elm tree, with the stream purling beneath green veils of weeping willow and the white light of the sun dazzling on all the stooks that the reapers had piled in the cornfield.

There was one such day but whether it was the day of the chase with the gangers I no longer remember. At this distance all those days blend into one with men playing cricket on the village green and the smell of mint coming from the river bed on summer evenings and the only thing that counted was to be with Uncle Victor.

He was my hero, if you want the truth.

You ask, what could there be in common between a boy of ten and an old man rising seventy? It is hard to put into words but we were wonderfully close together. For Uncle Victor was never bored, always bubbling with enthusiasm. He seemed to have done everything and to have been everywhere. He knew not only about wild flowers and birds and butterflies but about old books and strange dishes and faraway lands. Everything about him was strange, yet practical, from the stout ash stick he used when walking—yet who but Uncle Victor would have bought it from a gipsy ?—to the even stouter elastic-sided boots he wore, the soles studded with nails.

Even twenty-five years ago they were hopelessly old-fashioned but if a man is going to get up at three on a summer's morning and walk for hours to hear the dawn chorus and see the sunrise he has need of stout boots.

Often I heard my father chaff him because the maps he carried along with him on our walks were as old-fashioned as his boots, though there was fun in feeling the land come alive and to learn that the farm in the next valley, which had always been " the farm" to us had been called Cold Roast Farm in the time of Waterloo and probably was still.

" Site of an old Civil War battle here," Uncle Victor would grunt as we trudged over some field all tussocks and hummocks. " Not in the main reference books—found it in an old gazetteer last night. Just a little local skirmish . . . but if we had a spade and dug long enough I'd bet a pound to a pumpkin we'd find a Roundhead skull."

You had a hallowed desire to walk on tiptoes then, to think of the unshriven dead piled beneath your feet.

At other times, though, the maps proved false friends to us and we would set off trying to guide ourselves by a series of landmarks with old country names like Brockett's Hollow and Reeve's Rest, only to find that the one was now the site of a new housing estate and the other a filling station. Uncle Victor, though, often complicated the matter by recognising the existence of the new growth while pinning the old name on it. So to him, when asking the way, it would become the " Brockett's Hollow Housing Estate " or the " Reeve's Rest Filling Station," despite the locals having given them new names altogether and not taking kindly to them being altered.

It didn't help either when asking the way that Uncle referred to our part of the world as " Chussex," which he said was its correct name in the old Saxon divisions of England but still tended to confuse people fourteen centuries after.

Many was the good swingeing argument Uncle Victor had with a farmer or storekeeper, with the new man on the spot insisting that we were on private property and Uncle maintaining that if a footpath had run this way in William IV's time it ran this way still. A rich rare flow of invective he had then, something which was all his own but which depended like a sergeant-major in the Guards not on swear words but on the tone of voice he used.

"A measly moping lily-livered Stiggins," I heard him call one landowner who reminded him, I suppose, of the soapy clergyman in *Pickwick*, and a commercial traveller we met in a train was "a monolithic chunk of snobbocracy."

My father would have it that with his old maps Uncle Victor was just asking to get lost and I never heard Uncle deny it outright. "Never underrate the pleasures of the unexpected," he would say and it was true though it may seem laughable to say so.

Many a time we would set off on a cut-and-dried walk with the map doing all the work for us and then suddenly a footpath would appear from nowhere and Uncle Victor would decide that this way lay enchantment and soon we would be in a deep exciting wood that we had never found before, going we knew not where. In all those years my bedtime gradually advanced for though it had been seven-thirty prompt when the walks began it was often at that hour that Uncle would hit upon a short-cut that would get us home in no time and we would end the day as we had begun it—lost in another pitch-dark wood miles from anywhere.

But once on a hot summer night we heard the nightingale in an enchanted glade and on the darkest night of one December we battled our way across the downs in a snowstorm, our cheek-wet with the cold death-like kiss of the snow. And at both those times I know we were silent, feeling closer to something greater than ourselves.

Now it is a strange thing that if you want someone to do something with all your might and they achieve it through another's influence you at once think of a dozen reasons why it was not such a good idea. So far as my father was concerned I could read what I liked and since I liked best to read the adventures of Billy Bunter and Sexton Blake with my shilling a week pocket-money he made no real protest. Often he suggested I was welcome to read anything in his library of classics, which was a big one, but somehow the bindings and the old-fashioned print put me off.

But Uncle Victor—well, he was clever on that score. He began by reading my Sexton Blakes with me and a fine time we had deep in the ferns on some sunny afternoon imagining ourselves in the fog of Baker Street with the great detective and Pedro the bloodhound and the Rolls-Royce known as the Grey Panther parked at the kerb ready to speed off to Whitechapel and put the " agents of a foreign power " where they belonged.

Then one afternoon, as if by accident, Uncle Victor pulled a book from his pocket, opened it and read :

There was one stone face too many up at the château . . . it lay back on the pillow of Monsieur le Marquis. It was like a fine mask, suddenly startled, made angry and petrified. Driven home into the heart of the stone figure attached to it was a knife. . . .

And I still remember the pleasant tingle of horror that ran through me as Uncle Victor, closing the book with a snap, repeated with blood-chilling emphasis the message that the haft had plunged home :

Drive him fast to his tomb. This, from JACQUES.

" Go *on*," I said, " read what happened next."

" No good reading what happened next," Uncle Victor countered, "until you've read what happened before. Here, take it home and see what you make of it. It's not a bad thriller."

A little disrespectful to Charles Dickens, perhaps, but that was how my interest was first aroused in *A Tale of Two Cities*. And after that came *Ivanhoe* and *Oliver Twist* and *Silas Marner* and *David Copperfield*—all thanks to that simple little ruse of Uncle Victor's.

Funnily enough my father now often said that it wouldn't do me a scrap of harm to read a few " twopenny bloods," as boys' thrillers were called then, and he even went out of his way to buy me a few if he passed a newsagent. But a little jealousy is human in a father and I think he felt hurt that Uncle Victor had prevailed with me where he had not. For my father had worked hard all his life to give me the best and Uncle Victor was reckoned the least successful member of a large family.

And my mother told me, not laying great emphasis on it but laughing a little, " I shouldn't take everything that Uncle Victor says as gospel if I were you. I know he's had a fascinating life but you couldn't really use it as a model."

Now that was true enough. Even at ten I could see that all through life Uncle Victor had given way to the same impulses that he did on our walks—with a fresh career every so often presenting as tempting a prospect as an unknown footpath.

To begin with he had been a lawyer in practice on his own but at thirty, after throwing a man who was blackmailing a woman down a flight of stairs, he sold up everything and decided that acting was the life. " I was too honest to be a lawyer," was the way he dismissed that. And an actor-playwright he became, in the good old days of the fit-up theatres when the company moved from rented hall to rented hall, playing *The Rosary* and *East Lynne* and sometimes having to come down off the stage to toss out the roughs in the audience before the show could go on. So an actor had to be tough indeed. But even the little company of eight were not tough enough to withstand the wrath of the British Fleet in the week they played Portsmouth, the week that Uncle strode on in the second act of *Uncle Tom's Cabin* and told Little Eva : " 'Twas I that shot your dog." The sailors never knew that Uncle thought he was Captain Horace Garside in the third act of *Temptations of an Actress* for at that point they tore up the theatre by the roots.

And then Uncle Victor was a novelist, avowing, three weeks after the publishers had withdrawn his novel because of some libel suit pending, that he was " a hundred years ahead of his time," and after that an inventor, patenting a non-collapsible deck-chair though the company soon went into liquidation when people began to write in describing their bruises, and finally a market gardener more renowned for his green fingers than for his tact as a salesman. For once twenty-five people called in a morning to buy tomatoes and Uncle Victor inquired sharply of the twenty-sixth: " By Cæsar and Cleopatra, does the whole bloody town want tomatoes ? " Which was just his way and not a scrap of harm to it, but business was never quite the same after.

If Uncle Gilbert, the grocery king, had not given him a good allowance in the days I am recalling I shudder to think where he would have ended. For Uncle Victor was as generous as a drunken tinker with money or help, pressing the contents of his wallet on an unemployed man to tide him over until he got work or carrying a heavy basket of laundry all the way up a steep hill to help an old woman. The one thing you would never do was scare him for when a gang of louts came thundering at his door one Christmas Eve, pretending to be carol singers and demanding money or the windows would get broken, he was out among them with his walking-stick like an avenging angel and sent them running for dear life.

A good old man he was, and if he achieved little that was material in life at least he drained the cup to the last drop. And he took the scales from my eyes and taught me to see the world around with a wonder that has never left me.

Only the bond that was between us was so strong that it could not last without trouble, if you appreciate the paradox.

And the day it came to a head between him and my parents I remember well for it was the day he saved my life, the day I almost died.

CHAPTER TEN

THE RICHEST MAN IN THE FAMILY

It is pretty to see what money will do

SAMUEL PEPYS

WE HAD all gone to the drawing-room after breakfast that morning. Four of us sitting there—my father, my mother, Uncle Victor and myself—and not a smile between us.

"Well, that's the long and short of it," my father was saying. "Either you undertake to get him back here by six or we shall have to put a stop to it."

"Definitely a stop," my mother added.

If both my parents were angry, perhaps they had reason. Snow had lain upon the valley for weeks now yet it had not stopped Uncle Victor and me from going too far. Day after day in that bitter weather we had walked as usual, with him thundering on our door with his old ash stick as early as eight a.m.; night after night we had been late home. Once Uncle Victor's old-fashioned turnip watch had stopped and we had missed the bus. Once we had taken a "short-cut" which proved disastrous. There was a night when my father had put on gumboots to come and look for us and several nights when human charity and the lateness of the hour demanded that Uncle Victor, ravenous for cold ham and pickles and whisky and soda, bed down with us for the night.

"It's all right in the summer," my father said. "Come home at any hour you like within reason. But walking in the snow

. . . tramping in here at all hours for late dinner . . . you'll wear the boy out . . ."

" If we *ever* had any idea of when you were coming," my mother said, " but we *never* know . . . winter or summer."

She was right, of course. In the three years we had been together we had played shameful havoc with the peaceful calendar of my parents' lives. We were almost never on time for meals and the attachment between us had grown so strong that I now saw Uncle Victor at other times than in school holidays. Once he had turned up to see me unexpectedly when my parents were giving a tennis-party, an alien argumentative figure in that summery crowd. At times the house held the faint smell of stagnant water from all the jars of newts and liquifying toadstools we brought into it.

I was twelve years old and after taking a fond farewell of the Chaileys I had left Waterton House for my public school. Unfortunately for my parents it was a day school which gave me a lot of time to see Uncle Victor.

" I never object to seeing any Collier in this house," my father said into the awkward silence, " but I like to know where I am. . . ."

My mother sniffed. She was less agreeable to seeing Colliers invade the house now than she had been. At different times recently she had seen not only Uncle Victor but a great deal of my Uncle Percy and my Cousin Burton. Uncle Percy was a heavily-built man with a ginger moustache and a hearty laugh who claimed to be a member of the British Secret Service. My mother could not raise a smile at the joke—if he meant it as a joke—any more than she could raise a smile at his mysterious references to " X," his chief, his habit of using our address to send messages in code to Stanley Baldwin, the Prime Minister or his long involved story of an admiral he had caught passing on naval secrets to a Russian princess. He said he had achieved this by resigning from his club after pretending to cheat at cards and disguising himself as a costermonger. She cared even less for Cousin Burton, a railways enthusiast, who wore a sports jacket stained with diesel oil, spent his spare time walking along disused branch lines and avowed that fate left a man only two alternatives—whether he was going to spend his life waiting for a woman or a train.

And suddenly all of it had boiled up into this ultimatum—a six o'clock curfew. . . .

"We could be back by six," I volunteered, trying to stave off the sense of quarrel that was brooding.

"You're not concerned with this argument," my father said, looking meaningly at Uncle Victor.

"Ah, well, yes," Uncle Victor said, waking to life. He looked somehow pathetic that morning, still with his old fishing hat clapped on his head. But no one had suggested he remove it, perhaps because he was no longer welcome. "Subject to emergencies, six o'clock by all means . . ."

"There *are* no emergencies," my father said angrily. "Suppose I only got home to dinner each night subject to emergencies. Where would Eveline be? It's six o'clock or nothing."

So on that note we set off but I think I knew in my bones even then that something would go wrong.

It was cold up on the hills that day and the snow was so bright that it hurt your eyes, as white as icing sugar as we crunched through it. But the air was like wine in our blood and we would have felt good if it had not been for the sense that our friendship hung in the balance.

"Of course," Uncle Victor said once, though he was talking much less than usual this morning, "your father's right. You should have more friends of your own age."

This was puzzling for it was not what my father had said. He knew that I had several friends of my own age. The chief among them were Stuart, whose father owned a chain of shoe shops, and Eric, whose father had "run away from Mummy." That was how he had confided it to us in break one morning, flushed with shame and tears misting his spectacles, so that Stuart and I had tried to comfort him with barley sugar and now we shared most things. Disguised with false moustaches, false noses and a false bald head we spent long days stalking the grocer in my village, whom we believed to be a German spy.

" Well, of course," said Uncle Victor vaguely when I pointed this out, " just the same . . ."

" We're jolly well not going to let anyone split us up, are we ? " I said, trying to sound stout-hearted.

" No question of that," Uncle Victor said. " But there are a lot of factors to consider. . . ."

I pretended not to know what he meant. But in my heart I think I knew. He was not going to fight the issue and for me to have more school friends was the answer. He was too old and too tired and all his life there had been so much fighting.

Just the same a kind of desperation seemed to overtake him. For that morning we walked farther than I can ever remember. The cottages and the farms dropped behind, silent and blanketed under the snow, and we came to a strange wild country stretching for miles with the birch trees like black lattice-work against a sky of iron. No sound but the creaking of our boots on the snow and no clue as to where we might eat until we saw the inn.

Standing alone on a great sandy knoll it was, a small stone alehouse with a bench outside it and a slate roof, and the one thing to surprise you above all was to find an inn like that miles from anywhere. So we trudged towards it, through the silence, Uncle Victor explaining that it must have been built for the wood-cutters long ago, and when we pushed in through the door of the only bar the noise and the heat and the fog of shag tobacco was like a blow in the face. There was a gamekeeper or two and a policeman who had come from nowhere and a group of foresters at the dart-board and a gipsy smoking a clay pipe and somehow, I don't know why, with my boyish eyes it seemed the most wonderful inn I had ever seen.

And there was the landlord, a big man in a cardigan with a waxed moustache, saying " No private room, I'm afraid, guv'nor . . . and if the lad's under age . . ." Then the constable was appealed to and suddenly Uncle Victor was ordering drinks and great pint mugs of beer with the deep golden glow of dandelions were frothing along the bar and it was all right for me to stay " just this once." There was no hot food but a cold

round of rare roast beef and mustard pickles for us to help ourselves to as we would. And the gipsy thought Uncle Victor had
a lucky face and wanted the honour of drinking his health and
the King's health, too, so there was more beer ordered and I was
going to have a shandy-gaff as usual but one of the foresters
said "Nip o' ale on a nasty day like this'n wun't hurt the lad
none." But I wondered what my mother would say.

So the pewter mug came up with the beef and pickles and
sitting at a scrubbed wooden table, eating and finding the drink
good and feeling sleepy but liking the bitter nuttiness of it, washing
my tongue and feeling proud to be sitting there, a man among men,
I thought this was the real England and I wanted this moment to
live for ever, knowing it must die. And the bobby ruffled my hair
affectionately and said, "'E'll soon be sinkin' 'is pint with the best
of 'em, eh?" And we were all friends, true friends and you must
not laugh when I say that in this moment, not even knowing one
another's names, we loved one another.

And we walked away at last, warm with the glow of fellowship,
relishing the ice in the wind, with their laughter and farewells
ringing behind us and I swore even then, One day I will go
back. And years later—though this is another story—I tried
but I could never find the way and the people thereabouts looked
at me strangely for the description reminded them of no inn they
had ever known in those parts.

So perhaps it was a dream, our enchanted inn with the white
snow lying—but I think I became a man, that day upon the hill.

.   .   .

But the rest of the afternoon—well, that was desperation.
For the snow began to fall again with the sky a great leaden bowl
above our heads. And as everything had touched the heights
for one brief hour so it now began to go abysmally wrong. I
hurt my foot in a rabbit-hole and Uncle Victor's old watch gave
out on us again, so by the time we came out on the main road
a long time after, it was four o'clock and the bus we wanted
had gone.

We looked at one another then, knowing that we would not be home by six and all that this meant.

Then suddenly—for it was my idea—I saw a gleam of hope. For there was a wood within ten minutes and through it, I knew, a path led straight and true down chalk slopes to the river. And there, spanning the river in a world of night, where the yew trees stretched black arms across the water, was a line of stepping stones.

If we could only cross there—and quickly before the light fell —there was a fast coach service to take us home in no time at all.

To do him justice Uncle Victor argued against it with all his might but I urged it with all of mine as the only way. At last he said, " Well, all right, old son—but are you sure your foot's up to it ? You seem to be limping a bit."

I had wrenched my ankle in the rabbit-hole and the pain was like a band of hot steel but I pretended to remove a pebble in my shoe and after that to walk normally. The pain was worse than ever then, of course, but Uncle Victor, with the long sight of a falcon, could see less clearly close at hand and I traded shamelessly on that.

At any rate we made good going and there were the stepping stones, in the grey luminous light, stretching like white crosses across the inky swollen water.

" Now very gently does it," said Uncle Victor. " I'll go first."

And across those stones he went, as lightly as a hare for all that he would be seventy next birthday, and seeing him go like that I gained confidence. All went well until we were in mid-stream and I was trying to keep balanced and not look at the black water lapping or hear the dinning of the weir, when my toecap skidded on a patch of ice. I slipped, putting all my weight on my hurt ankle ; it gave and I was falling.

Then I was in the river up to my neck, fighting not to go under, with the force of the current pounding me against the stone pillar, clinging to the top of it for dear life with the ice like a savage hand driving all the breath from my body.

Then Uncle Victor gave a great shout, seeing me, and in a

minute he was skipping back, almost stumbling but sure-footed as ever, and he was saying something but the paralysing cold and the noise of the weir blotted all of it out. But he lay down, flat on his belly on the stones, and his arms came into the water round me, heaving and straining in the falling night.

And I don't remember getting out of the water at all, so great was the pain but somehow he got me upright again on the stones steering me across to the other side for there was a hotel only minutes away.

Once again that day he persuaded a landlord to break the rules, this time about licensing hours, so that within minutes cherry brandy was going like sweet fire down my throat. He was on the phone, too, ordering a car, for I was blue with cold, shaking and gasping with cold, weeping with the pain of the blood quickening life in my limbs. But because his house was nearer he took me back there and not to ours.

Then it all blurs. A draughty car ride and the glow of blood fading again . . . the lights on the porch of his little house . . . a great fire glowing in the grate of his old study with the leather-bound books and the deep arm-chairs and the decanters . . . and then a swooping sickness of pain and cold and desolation as the heat wrapped around me like a blanket. All these, and a sense of falling.

But I remember he caught me and as I went backwards into blackness, not caring, there was one image too hard and bright for time to wear away : his voice saying over and over, " Hold up, old son . . . dear, dear old son, hold up " and a thing I never saw before or since, the tears running like spring rain down his old lined face.

.   .   .

Strangely enough, after that I saw as much of Uncle Victor as ever I could wish. My parents had no choice. I was months on the old bed that Uncle Victor had fitted up in his study, ill with bronchitis and threatened pneumonia, too ill, the doctor said, to be moved. Then there were ulcers in my throat, so I could barely swallow or breathe. The snow had gone from the land and the lilac was a white fragrant waterfall in Uncle Victor's little front garden before I saw the outside world again.

My mother moved into the house the very night I was taken ill, arriving white-faced and distraught in the old Daimler hire-car. At first her anger with Uncle Victor was a terrible thing to see, cold and unrelenting. For weeks she would scarcely allow him entry to his own study while she nursed me and did everything for me, sitting beside me to sponge my burning forehead or making cool jugs of lemonade to moisten my parched throat. Day or night she would not leave my side while Uncle Victor could do little more than pace the hallway, as anxious for bulletins as an expectant father and feeling as much in the way.

But it could not last. The worry and intensity of her feelings were so great that my mother's health broke. For one whole week she could not come at all.

Then old Dr. Paine took a hand—gruff old Dr. Paine who still took snuff, who had looked after us all since the time when I was teething and who believed that country walks and fresh-picked vegetables were the cure for most things. It was he who made my mother see how dependent my recovery was on Uncle Victor so that little by little she softened. She still made the four-mile journey each day but every night now she returned to sleep.

Only, as any mother would, she contented herself with saying, " Darling, you'll be well enough to come home soon. I promise . . . and I'll cook you all your favourites again . . . calves' liver and bacon and Irish stew and treacle pudding . . . you'll like that, won't you ? "

" Yes, Mum," I would say, so as not to hurt and glad that the light in the study was always dim. For I felt that my face must mirror the lie.

I loved my mother and father truly but when it came to going home my heart was full of conflict. For now I was indeed part of Uncle Victor's world and though at first he slept upstairs in his own room it wasn't long before he had moved his bed down to the study, too, to act as night nurse if need be. And though I chafed at the need to lie in bed, and the sweet steaming bowls of Friar's Balsam and the anti-phlogiston compresses were a sore trial, I loved that study.

The house itself was a snug red-brick temple of middle-class comfort but that study was something apart—a room that Uncle Victor had unconsciously created as an extension of his own personality. As masculine as the Silence Room of a club it was, with its deep leather arm-chairs, its Welsh dresser hung with pewter and blue-and-white china, its sombre rows of leather-bound books. It was shabby enough in all conscience but comfortably shabby, with a blue porcelain jar of wild birds' feathers that Uncle Victor used for cleaning his pipe, set squarely on the great mahogany desk that was always littered with dried plants and old maps and the frail shells of birds' eggs. There was no central lighting at all—just red-shaded table-lamps, set here and there at intervals, to cast a soft orange glow that helped the firelight.

In the first weeks of the illness the fever was so high and the fluid so thick on my lungs that I scarcely cared whether I ate or not, but as I grew stronger, before the ulcers came to choke my throat, Uncle Victor began to cook for me. And it was here that I had to do some lying to save my mother's feelings.

It wasn't that Uncle Victor cooked more exotic dishes than my mother but once get him at the stove with meat and spice and vegetables and a copper saucepan or two and he had a sorcerer's touch. There was a little herb garden down behind his bean row, neat green phalanxes of mint and camomile and tarragon, and whatever Uncle Victor was cooking it always called for a few hasty trips to the herb garden. Mint for the first new potatoes, of course, but then the omelet needed a touch of chervil, the salad must have its tarragon while the salad bowl needed just a breath of garlic.

" How about a dish of sweetbreads and some parsley sauce, old son ? . . . or tripe *à la mode* . . . I'll do it in cider with a cow-heel and just a dash of brandy . . . that'll stick to your ribs."

Whenever I could be left he did a short stiffish walk for exercise, but only for a few miles, so anxious was he to return.

I liked it best when he came back after his walk on a sharp evening and we talked, sleepily and with perfect understanding, before the evening meal.

The kettle would be boiling on the tiny spirit stove he kept beside his desk : he was always mixing himself Dickensian drinks with lots of boiling water and Demerara sugar—rum and clove cordial or gin and hot water with a dash of peppermint.

" How many miles did you do to-night ? "

" Oh . . . not above three or four . . . I was a poor thing to-night."

" Not like walking to Ludlow that time . . . tell me about that breakfast."

" What, at the old Feathers ? You don't get breakfasts like that nowadays . . . a pigeon pie, half a York ham, a loaf and a half of bread and five pints of coffee."

" *Three* pints . . . you said *three* pints before."

" Well, perhaps it was three . . . memory plays tricks."

A strange household, I always thought it, for though there were four of them living there together they seemed to have no point of contact at all. My Aunt Kate, a faded little button of a woman, moved through the dimly-lit house as if in a trance, smiling gently and murmuring a kindly word if she chanced to see you, which was not often, overlooking the cleaning woman to a degree, cooking some of the meals. But she did not cook for Uncle Victor, whose hours were uncertain. She cooked for Uncle William Henry when he returned, late as always, from business, and for my Aunt Helen Victoria.

I was always terrified of Aunt Helen Victoria, though I do not know why. Perhaps it was because, although she was not ill, she never left her room upstairs. In the big best bedroom with its green silk hangings and its faint smell of pot-pourri, the curtains almost always drawn to shut out the light of day, she lived a strange existence like some delicate piece of tapestry so old it must be preserved under glass. Propped against pillows she half-lay, half-reclined in bed, the delicate lacework shawl she always wore setting off the handsome aquiline face, the piercing grey eyes, the beautifully-kept silver hair.

" Come here, little Dickie," she would command, her voice rich and resonant like an old-time actress's, and when I had groped my way through the half-light towards her, half-hypnotised by those compelling grey eyes, she would take my hand in a grip like iron—a surprising grip for a hand as yellow and fragile as parchment, delicately traced with blue veins.

" Your old aunt has been disappointed, little boy," she would say, " bitterly disappointed . . . you must take care, you know, a lad like you . . . a heart is a tender responsibility and to betray a young girl's trust is wanton wickedness."

This made no sense to me at the age of nine, when I heard it first. I knew very few young girls to trust or distrust me and I could not think how I had disappointed her. It was my father who explained to me that Aunt Helen Victoria had been disappointed in love fifty years before by the music master at the mixed school which she owned. But the master, my father thought, had been quite unaware of the passion.

After that she had withdrawn by degrees from the world altogether, refusing almost all visitors except my father, whom she still summoned to her bedside and called " little Charles." Then she would press his hand fervently and tenderly, to his great embarrassment, the same advice concerning a young girl's trust as she gave to me.

" I often think Helen Victoria sees herself as a kind of Miss Havisham," my father said once, but I had not read *Great Expectations* so this meant nothing to me then.

But it was not her but Uncle William Henry who was causing my Uncle Victor such anxiety at the time I am writing of. I saw most of that episode from my bed in the study and I have not forgotten it.

Indeed it set the whole family by the ears and shocked them so profoundly that they never dared tell Aunt Helen Victoria about it at all.

It must have been well into the small hours of one morning and the first thing I remember is waking to hear voices.

" I wouldn't have plagued you for the world, my dear old friend, but I seem to have lost my key."

"William Henry, I've told you before it's all right. Just get to bed before I do you a mischief."

"Ah-ha, *but* . . ." it sounded as if Uncle William was being strangely coy ". . . I have a secret to impart, old friend, if you'll bear with me . . . mind, it's not exactly definite but I think, yes, *think*—a certain lady is rather partial to yours truly."

He was not in the least drunk but he was mellow and talkative and I could hear Uncle Victor's patience wearing thin.

"For pity's sake, William Henry, this is no hour for riddles. What tomfoolery have you been up to?"

"Well, now, I can bank on your discretion, can't I, old friend? Mum's the word for the moment but I think a certain lady might not be averse to calling herself Mrs. William Henry Collier."

This was too much for Uncle Victor. "You silly old goat, you must be tipsy! You come home by taxi in white tie and tails at two a.m. and tell me some flibberty-gibbet wants to marry you. How old did you tell her you were?"

"To tell the truth, we've always rather kept off age," Uncle William Henry admitted. "But these little ladies, you know, they like a man who's mature."

"You crazy old goat," Uncle Victor roared. "You must be off your chump. You're rising seventy and you'll be the death of us all. You'll tell me next you've been in some bistro drinking champagne out of her slipper."

"It was the Savoy," said Uncle William Henry, rather hurt. "And Clicquot '28—a very good tipple at that." So saying he departed for bed.

I went to sleep then but I remembered soon enough when I woke next morning. It was so out of keeping with Uncle William Henry I could think of little else.

For Uncle William Henry was generally reckoned to be the richest man in our family, with a fortune not far short of Uncle Gilbert's. Money was the ruling passion of his life. Ever since my father could remember, Uncle William Henry, as head of the family, had never arrived in the City of London later than eight a.m. and he rarely left before eight at night. He boasted that he was the only man in the City who could negotiate a deal with the charwoman scrubbing the floor round his feet.

A funny wizened little man, he was, almost bald, with a neat grey moustache and a habit of wagging his forefinger at you as he talked. He was the only man I ever saw in my boyhood still wearing button boots and at home, in a velvet smoking-jacket and a skull cap, puffing at the clay pipe he always smoked for economy's sake, he seemed even stranger. But the family accepted these little quirks, and what was more they accepted that Uncle William Henry was very rich indeed.

Even stranger, for I was young, I never believed that he was. Life was cut-and-dried to me then: a rich man smoked cigars and lived in style and the idea of a man who had piled up a fortune walking a mile to work across the City of London, taking short-cuts through stifling alleys to save his bus fare made no sense to me. But of course such men have existed and grown rich smoking clay-pipes and taking short-cuts, as my parents pointed out. It never shook my father's faith that when Uncle William Henry invited him to lunch he took him not to a City chop-house but to a cheap dining-room by the docks at Hay's Wharf.

" William Henry was always as close as a crofter," my father said once. "Things weren't good when he took over the family and he had to be careful. But he's made up for it all right."

" But Dad," I queried, " is he really rich ? "

" I should say the old fox is salting it away," my father said. " Look at the hours he works. A man doesn't drive himself like that all these years unless he's getting something out of it."

I asked Uncle Victor how much he thought his brother had put away. " If he isn't worth £50,000, I'm a Hottentot," he replied promptly.

Still, I couldn't believe it. To me he was a good enough little man, though his presence could jar if you had too much of him, who liked to be mysterious and talk about " recessions " and " selling at par " and the market " getting bearish." It struck me as funny yet tragic at the same time that even his family, men like my father who had a good deal to say in the running of the country, knew so little about stocks and shares that they saw Uncle William Henry as a kind of pantomime genie.

Because he knew the right magic phrases they thought he could take their pennies and transfer them into pounds in a twinkling if he just so wished it. But I noticed that Uncle William Henry always avoided using the personal pronoun. "Someone made a nice little packet to-day," he would say but I often wondered if it was he. He never even gave a tip direct— just "If a certain old friend wants to do himself a bit of good he might start thinking about rubber."

If you asked him point-blank, as like as not he would only say, "That needs a little consideration," nodding and smiling and wagging his forefinger.

And now, after all these years as a bachelor, his only leisure a little walking and poring over old copies of *The Stock Exchange Year Book*, life was taking on a new meaning for him. He had given up the clay pipe and turned to cigars. He had bought himself an opera cape lined with red silk. He was taking dancing lessons from the famous Santos Casani.

The family invited him to bring his bride-to-be down to tea one Sunday. They were as certain as could be that he had made a will in her favour, and that she knew it.

They were certain, too, that she held the key to the one mystery that had always eluded them—what Uncle William Henry did for a living.

For though it may seem absurd, in my boyhood families were far more retiring about what the breadwinner did and what he earned and when my father was a boy it was even more so. As head of the family Uncle William's status in the City had been accepted, his long hours of industry were a legend and though they had been curious at times as to just what he did up there they had long since ceased to ponder it. "Nobody ever really liked to," as Aunt Kate once said.

But there was one person who did like to and that was Miss Dora Popplewell, Uncle William Henry's betrothed.

She was all right in her way, I suppose : she liked to laugh a lot and show her teeth and she was always very smart, in black tailored costumes with pockets which flared away on a slant, which my mother said privately were " common." I never knew her age though I guessed it to be half Uncle William's, but her hair was a rich russet colour, perhaps natural, perhaps not. Her scent was always parma violets, strong and rather sweet, not like the crisp astringent scents my mother used. She was secretary to a garment wholesaler and had met Uncle William Henry when they were both sheltering in a doorway from the rain.

But if she was suspect with the family they gave her plenty of good Collier hospitality the first Sunday she came down : a tea to make the tables groan and plenty of the sensible food a tea should include besides jam and cake ; sweet radishes and lettuce hearts and hot buttered toast spread with Gentleman's Relish and Aunt Kate's sausage rolls. If I search until I die I will never find sausage rolls like those, with just a thin nutty coating of short-crust pastry that left a faint dust on your fingers, wrapped round a fat pork sausage.

My father and mother were there too, and Dora went out of her way to charm all of them, smiling her very wide smile and laughing loudly and wiping her eyes at everyone's jokes, sitting beside Uncle William Henry and sometimes patting his hand. He called her " my Poppy " and everybody looked surreptitiously to see if she was wearing a ring. But she wasn't so my father said afterwards, " Perhaps there's hope yet."

But on the whole I think the party went off well and the only awkward moment came when Dora was sitting down to tea and Aunt Kate awoke from one of her trances and said, "Come along now, my dear . . . I expect you'd like to sit with the light behind you." She always said that to every woman visitor, my mother included, but from what I heard Dora liked it even less than my mother did.

Mind you, she was always very good with me, spending a lot of time on the end of my bed talking about films and books and bringing me enormous boxes of Cadbury's King George V chocolates bound with a red bow that my mother took away and rationed out. " The old soldier " was her name for me because we had a joke that I was in bed getting over campaign wounds.

Oddly enough, just lying in bed, I could see that both sides thought the other was gaining ground when they weren't. When Uncle William Henry bought Dora a half hoop of diamonds as an engagement ring at Mappin and Webb's the whole family were beside themselves. There were so many recriminations, with everyone swearing that she must be a wicked fast woman after his money, that Aunt Kate burst into tears and called Uncle William " a wayward boy."

Yet Dora, on her side, was just as worried, believing there was a conspiracy on foot against her, when there was none. Indeed the family had no plan at all.

" Well," she said, perched on the end of my bed one night, " what do they think of me ? "

" The family ? Well, they like you," I said. What else could I say ?

" Oh, no," she said, her mouth twisting rather wryly. " Not little me. I'm properly in their bad books, I am."

I felt sorry for her then because she tried too hard and she always would. I didn't think she was " a fast woman " at all. I thought she was lonely and desperate and probably seeing even Uncle William Henry as her last chance.

" Well," I said, " why ask me ? "

She pinched my cheek. " Because you're the Old Soldier," she said, " and the Old Soldier sees what goes on. He just sits here with his books and watches and doesn't say much. And you're my Willie's favourite, aren't you ? "

" Not me," I said, never more surprised. " Uncle Victor's, p'raps. Uncle William thinks I ought to be a broker when I leave school."

" O—o—o—h," she said, then, her voice up a shade, " so that's what he wants you to be, eh ? An old broker. Follow in his illustrious footsteps, eh ? "

She said it so casually but even then I felt a little prick of triumph. Knowing what I did now, I was one up on the family.

" Well," I said, " I don't know."

Dora tried to look unconcerned. " You know," she said, " trust's a funny thing . . . I mean, right from the moment I met Willie I just trusted him completely because some people you can . . . I trusted him so much I never even thought to ask him what he does to earn an honest penny. Isn't that funny ? "

" He's in the City," I told her.

" Oh, I know that," she said a little bitter. " His family may think we're out having high jinks every night but if I see him more than once a week I'm a lucky girl. My own fiancé, mind. But I mean he spends enough hours in his precious old City, what does he *do* there ? "

" I don't know," I said. " Nobody knows."

Dora looked at me with less friendship. " Oh, come on ! I'm not so green I'm a cabbage, dear. You mean you've promised not to tell, is that it ? "

" Honest," I said, " I don't know. Nobody has ever since Uncle William Henry began in business."

" Well, I never heard of anything so potty," said Dora sharply. " And why all this Uncle William Henry ? Uncle William or Uncle Henry but the two together just sounds silly."

" It was so as not to mix him up with Uncle William Francis," I told her, " though *he* died years ago. Hey, wasn't it a joke, the old chap ended up thinking he'd invented the crossword puzzle but it did no harm so they let him think it."

" I'll tell you one thing," said Dora with force, " I think this family's going to give me the pip."

From that moment, diamond ring or no, nothing would do but Dora must find out what Uncle William Henry did. First she tried asking him for his office phone number and suggesting she should meet him from work. Each time he managed to fob her off but her irritation was beginning to mount. She began to find fault with his habits and his working hours and she no longer laughed at his little jokes.

" Oh, sweetie, not *that* one again," she would cry, " We've *heard* it, darling, donkey's years ago, don't you *remember* ? "

And Uncle William Henry still nodded and smiled and wagged

his forefinger but his eyes were the eyes of a hunted man. She was going to find out about him and he knew it. All his life he had been happy, wrapped in his cloak of secrecy, a man of mystery, but now he had met every man's match—a woman of determination. She was going to strip away that cloak of secrecy if it was the last thing she did.

It was spring now and I was more and more out of bed. But the day the car came to take me home I was still as wobbly on my legs as a half-drowned spider and to leave them all there in the little house after so long might have been a time for tears if I had been younger. And in any case Uncle Victor had promised to be over every day to see me.

But one morning not long after I heard the phone ring early and my father was talking for a long time before he came up to my bedroom, looking shaken. The first thing he said was, " That was Victor. I'm afraid he won't be over to-day or quite a few days . . . poor old William Henry died in the night."

There was a lump in my throat then, thinking of the little man but thinking at the same time, perhaps no one will ever know now. His secret has gone with him.

But of course it hadn't. He had taken his illusions with him and death had offered him the way out though I didn't know whether to laugh or cry when I heard, in passing, that he had died, quite peacefully, of a heart attack with a copy of *The Financial Times* spread out across the eiderdown. And it was days after that before I saw Uncle Victor again for all his time in the last forty-eight hours had been spent sorting through papers—whole deed-boxes full of papers, though most of them of no value, in an effort to find some clue as to Uncle William Henry's missing fortune.

For the cash in the bank amounted to little more than £200 and in his will he had left Dora a fifth of that and his platinum cuff-links.

No matter how they tried they couldn't make it more but my father and Uncle Victor, working together, did find some vital clue among the papers—the address of a firm somewhere off Throgmorton Street in the City of London. So straight away my father paid a visit there but he came home that night strangely quiet and not much inclined to talk.

For the firm knew of William Henry Collier very well; he had been with them fifty years and was one of their most valued employees.

They were an old-fashioned firm importing sultanas and he was their chief clerk.

The bank statements showed that he had spent the best part of five hundred pounds in the last few months playing at Romeo, but there had never been any more. He had never owned a stock or a share in his life.

When Uncle Victor told Dora over the phone he said there was only a kind of strangled sound before she hung up. I believe it was shock as much as anything for I think she would have done her best for him given the chance. Even my father, who had no personal interest in Uncle William's fortune, seemed to view it all in terms of deceit. " He had no right to mislead people like that," he said.

But had he? I never thought so. Strangers to the world of money, they had made him what he was. They had invested him with an importance he never had, and the illusion, which he had even come to believe himself, had brightened all the dusty years of his life.

Especially those long hours of overtime he had worked to the very end. A good worker, they told my father up there: first to come and last to leave. For fifty long years, working well but so slowly, it had taken him twelve hours of each day to do what younger, spryer men did in six.

CHAPTER ELEVEN

" MR. PUFFIN "

Do you think that the things people make
fools of themselves about are any less real
and true than the things they behave sensibly
about ?

GEORGE BERNARD SHAW
Candida

IT WAS a long time before my parents and Uncle Victor were
reconciled again. Family feeling had drawn them together when
Dora, as they thought, was all set to make a fool of Uncle William
Henry, but when that passed the relations between them were a
kind of cautious neutrality. No better people existed, but I
think they found it hard to forgive him for filling such a place
in my heart.

And now it was 1938 which meant that for me the all-important
Matriculation examination was one year off, with three hours'
homework to be done each night and at week-ends too. I was
wearing long trousers, much taken up with Rugby football and
boxing, so it was natural I saw Uncle Victor less. It didn't look
as if things could ever be the same again.

Then one June morning, coming down from the strawberry
bed across the tennis-lawn, I saw a cat.

We had fitted up a bird-table near our kitchen door, like every
other house in our district, with chunks of fat for the blue tits
and a coco-nut for them to swing on and crumbs and crusts
of bread for all comers. And that was where the cat was crouch-

ing, low on its belly, wolfing stale dry bread as if its life depended on it.

The closer I got the closer I could see that it did, for the ribs poked out from its wasted body like the slats of a venetian blind and the fur hadn't the sable sheen of a good stole but was spiky and dead as an old rug. A black and white tom it was, black all over save for a clean white shirt-front and stomach, with four dainty milk-white paws.

By now I was close enough for it to hear me and as it turned I saw the hunted terror shine in eyes the colour of muscatel grapes. In a flash it had gone, over the trellis and into the shrubbery, cringing on its belly like any hunted thing with ears back and a funny little stump of a tail that looked as if it had been chopped off short tucked between its legs. For a wonder my mother and Lucy hadn't seen it for the kitchen faced on the coal bunker but they were busy talking about a fête that was being held that Saturday.

" Mum," I said, " can I have a saucer of milk to put down ? There was a stray cat out there eating bread and I think it's starving."

I had to shout to make myself heard for the piano-tuner was in the house that morning, up and down, A flat, D sharp, on and on, to keep our Bechstein upright in trim. We rarely used it except when guests persuaded Mother to play selections from *Pinafore* or *The Pirates of Penzance* but a good piano was like the shoe-cleaning and the two fires lit—something that every house like ours had.

" Oh, *dear*," my mother said, her face clouding to sadness as always when she heard of anything hunted or trapped, and thinking perhaps of Santley Street, " Oh, *dear*. Yes, take some milk out and see if you can get it to drink some." She removed the muslin cover hung with glass beads that was always used to keep flies from the milk jug and poured a saucerful.

" I'll just have to leave it," I said. " It's as wild as wild. Scared stiff it was and you could see all its ribs."

" Oh, *don't*," my mother said, really feeling its pain. " Well, take the saucer out and leave it and we'll have to see. And remember—not a word to your father yet." And as I trod gingerly out to set down the saucer she was cautioning Lucy about not telling " the master."

It wasn't that my father didn't like cats. He felt for all animals but in much the same way as he felt for everything that mattered deeply to him—not wisely but too well. He was never more English than in this ; you could talk to him uneventfully enough about world affairs, playing bridge, vintage claret, all things which interested him but in which he had no emotional stake. But touch him on tender subjects—it might be the classics or cruelty to animals—and he reacted as passionately as he had done all those years ago when he was courting my mother.

Only recently he had so mortally offended our neighbour, Mr. Bunney, virtually ordering him from the house after a violent argument over the classics, that it had taken all the combined efforts of my mother and the vicar to restore peace. Yet still at intervals my father would fume, " He dared to sit there—*in a knitted waistcoat*—and tell me he couldn't read George Eliot ! "

" Oh, Charles, don't *care* so much," my mother would say, and my father would promise not to, but he went on caring about great injustices and small, about cruelties of any kind read in the newspapers. My mother would even skim the newspaper at breakfast in search of items that might set my father worrying and then tell him, before he left for the office, that he might have a better day, say, if he missed Page Three altogether.

So she was wise about the cat, you see, for unless we could find some way to help, it was likely that my father would only worry about its plight without power to alter it for better or worse.

" Darling, please don't care so much," my mother would say so often. " You *do* care too much, you know, and it isn't worth it."

And my father would answer, as he always did, taking her hand in his, " So long as I've got you, my dear, I don't really worry . . . you know, they broke the mould the day they made you."

A thought to treasure in loneliness, indeed.

.   .

Not long after I saw the cat again. I was in a deck-chair under the syringa bushes, trying to make sense of Latin commentaries, but sitting where I could see the saucer of milk set down near the back door.

Each day when my father was safely off to the office, my mother had set this saucer down. Each evening she took it back in—untouched, noisy with flies, the milk curded with heat. Evidently the cat had not come.

Yet bread, crusts, fat, even the remains of a semolina pudding I had rejected had vanished from the bird-table. Was it all the birds ?

Suddenly from the corner of my eye I saw the cat come creeping. Stomach to the ground, tail down, ears back as if a blow was coming from nowhere. Then he stopped. He had seen the saucer. And I held my breath.

Cautiously he sniffed round its rim. A pink envelope of tongue slid out from beneath his whiskers. Then, even from where I sat, I could see a look that spoke of betrayal come into his eyes. A hurt look, as if we had played a cruel trick at the expense of his suffering. He moistened his lips because he was thirsty. Then he slunk away.

Though it sounds absurd, I felt the tears come to my eyes. The cat suspected a trick. He was used to filching dried bread, to drinking from rain puddles and water-butts. He did not know what milk was.

My mother and I pondered where it lived. " If we could find where it sleeps we could leave food there each day," my mother said. " Sparrow could send up some minced beef and I could cook it. . . ."

Among ourselves we discussed the problem a great deal, quieting our consciences by agreeing that we would tell my father when the time was ripe. As a result my father slept soundly at nights but my mother no longer did. Nor did I. At least once we would wake up and wonder how the cat was faring.

I watched the moonlight silvering school groups and boxing gloves and ink-stained Mark Twains, almost hating those emblems of comfort while something was suffering. Yet what could we do ? Put down food, of course, but a rat or a grey squirrel could get it as easily with us none the wiser.

That was as far as we had got until the afternoon of the tennis-party.

At least a dozen were there on that July Saturday sitting under the maple trees and if anybody had problems on their mind other than tennis they made a good job of concealing it. I say that because it was the same week that a man from the District Council had called on every family in the neighbourhood to teach us how to make a room gas-proof and to try on gas-masks, and my mother and father had scarcely talked for the rest of that day.

But the only mention of trouble all that afternoon was when Mr. Graveney, the bank manager, said, " I feel there are hopeful auguries, you know, that common-sense will prevail . . . very sound this man, Chamberlain, not the type to be bamboozled by dictators." Mr. Dyne, a senior official of the Colonial Office agreed, and my father added : " When it comes to a pinch, I think everyone's fundamentally decent enough to do the right thing." And that was the end of the matter.

Very formally attired the men were, compared with nowadays, with razor-edged white flannels and blazers with club colours and wearing Panama hats or straw boaters with club ribbons even when on the court. The women of my mother's age wore pleated white linen tennis dresses with shirt tops, coloured bandeaus in the style of Suzanne Lenglen and white stockings, though my Cousin Jasmine was wearing a blouse, white pleated shorts and ankle socks. But Jasmine was only twenty-three and as her mother said, " going through a phase." She liked to practise ballet on our front lawn when she was not sitting on the drawing-room floor talking about disarmament and the need to join the Peace Pledge Union.

Then there was Cousin Andrew, her brother, a quiet lad, always with a frown of concentration, who was going on to study engineering and had already dismantled our radio set for practice but in need of time to think about how to join it up again. Uncle Felix, their father, was there too, dressed for tennis like the rest but still holding the copy of *Pickwick* that he took almost everywhere, always ready to open it and read you a passage or two and finding such mirth in it still, and laughing so hard all the time he read that you couldn't hear a word though tears of joy were running down his own face. And his wife, Aunt Muriel, my mother's sister, was there, too, which meant they would all be driving home some time later that evening. For the country made her nervous to a degree that is impossible to describe ; set her down in Harrods for the day and she was as peaceful as you please but the sound of an owl hooting would keep her awake all night and the sight of a wasp on a dish of jam sent her almost into hysterics of fright.

There were one or two other professional men and their wives and there was Uncle Victor.

He had not been invited to the party but he had slogged four miles across the heath under a blazing sun to present my father with some spare snapdragon plants so it was only charity to offer him some tea.

I was sitting a little apart with him, drinking in the rich warm fragrance of sweet-williams, watching the game with my father playing, very tense and concentrated as he always was, his eye never off the ball, crouched and knees slightly bent. He had even played in the Wimbledon Plate so it was a test of skill to play with or against him, not only because he was good but because he always saw quicker than you where the ball would go and what you ought to do. And he cared so passionately, partner or opponent, that he could never resist telling you.

So now he served beautifully, tiptoe on the service line, a chopping overarm drive sliced so that the ball just skimmed the net and landed with a whiff of white dust right on the line of the left-hand court. Uncle Felix was running for return service but not fast enough, for my father shouted : " Up, get up, faster ! Backhand—use your backhand ! " And Uncle Felix was so taken aback that he lobbed the ball instead clean over the " tramlines " into the blackcurrant bushes, shouting " Blast it

all, Charles, don't try and help—you're playing *against* me."
And my mother said under her breath, "Oh, dear, I wish Charles
didn't *care* so much."

But as the ball landed plonk in the bushes I saw a scudding
streak of black-and-white fur and in that minute the stray cat
was away out of that retreat, fleeing like a demented thing towards
the shrubbery near the back door.

"Hallo," said Uncle Victor thoughtfully, the only one to
notice except me, "whose is the old puss-cat?"

I had just explained when my father shouted "Ball!" which
as usual was the signal for me to act as ball-boy. I had the
reward of a game later on but usually when the best players
had moved on to tall cold drinks.

As I dived head first into the bushes I saw Uncle Victor get
up and stroll off towards the shrubbery. He was still missing
when I got back.

But soon after Lucy came running, which she never did unless
something was amiss. I couldn't catch what she murmured to
my mother but I did hear my mother say, "Oh, good heavens,
what *is* he up to?" Then as discreetly as she could she hastened
off towards the kitchen. So I followed, curious, and Cousin
Jasmine came too.

When we got near the kitchen door it was a sight to remember
for years.

For there was Uncle Victor, mindless of the creases in his
suit, stretched almost flat on his stomach on the path of Cumberland stone and the fat pink thigh of a cold chicken put by for
that evening in his right hand. There was a saucer of milk on
the stones near him and all the time he kept up a soft soothing
flow of words like a groom rubbing down a horse: "Come
along, then, puss-cat . . . come along, old Fur-and-Whiskers
. . . come along. . . ."

And my mother said, "Oh, Victor, not the *chicken*," but
Uncle Victor motioned her to silence and we saw why.

Out of the bushes, timid and shrinking and belly dragging,
crept the cat. A pretty little thing it was, when you got close,
all skin and bone and hardly more than a kitten but with fine

white whiskers and pointed intelligent ears and the most melting green eyes I ever saw.

It saw Uncle Victor and it stopped. At once it was ready for flight. Then the rich roasted smell of the chicken caught its nose and it wavered, nostrils prickling, almost swooning with emptiness. For a silent minute fear fought with the anguish of hunger and hunger won. It crept forward and snatched the chicken, retreating to the shadow of a bush. It wolfed at the cold flesh, ungracefully, in a way that made you sick and angry to see such suffering.

In a moment it had crept to the saucer of milk. And as it began to lap, deciding to chance it, it began to purr for the first time, a rich rumbling note like a fine organ.

"Oh, poor little thing," Cousin Jasmine said. "Auntie, won't you adopt it and give it a home?"

"It looks just like a puffin," I said. "At the Zoo that time. We could call it Mr. Puffin."

And now the cat looked at us with big frightened eyes and began to mew. Not like a grown cat at all but a thin pitiful sound like a young seagull. *Hew, hew, hew*, it came, saying more plainly than any words, *Please don't hurt me*.

Just then my father joined the group, for the game was over. And the first thing he said, as he saw the cat at the saucer, was, "Well, thank God for that . . . someone's managed to get some food into that poor little devil."

"You've seen it before?" said my mother incredulously.

"I've watched it while I've been gardening," my father said. "It's the finest little mouser I've ever seen. I didn't say anything because I didn't want to upset you and Dick."

"Well," said my mother crossly, almost as if he had asked her to, "I shouldn't have stayed awake at night if I'd known *that*."

"Mum says we could adopt it and call it Mr. Puffin," I said, using a little low cunning. But no sooner had I spoken than Mr. Puffin, not liking all the attention he was receiving, snatched up the remains of the thigh and bolted into the bushes.

"I should think we could, couldn't we, Charles?" said my mother. "It wouldn't be too much trouble."

"Certainly I think it's time he had a pet," my father agreed. "But it looks like a case of first catch your cat . . ."

"Victor was marvellous," my mother said, looking more warmly at Uncle Victor than she had done for a long time. "How on earth he managed I don't know . . . though I must say that chicken's going to be a bit of a problem to-night."

"Chicken never agreed with me," my father said, lying in his teeth. "A little cold tongue will do me."

"I think," Uncle Victor said, "if you wouldn't mind my just popping over once in a while. . . ."

He took his leave of the tennis-party then. But next morning, soon after dawn, he was back in the garden. This time he had raided his own larder, even down to a half-pint bottle of milk. Mr. Puffin breakfasted off a cold chump chop left over from Uncle Victor's supper.

"Old Fur-and-Whiskers needs to get his strength back," he said when we invited him to breakfast.

"You don't think he'll develop rather expensive tastes?" asked my mother anxiously.

"Not a bit of it," Uncle Victor assured her. "Poor little bawbee's all skin and bone."

That night he came back with some cold veal and ham for Mr. Puffin's supper. When Mr. Puffin saw me in company with his benefactor he arched his back and hissed softly like a young swan. But inch by inch he crept back from the shrubbery to bolt his food and all the time Uncle Victor talked to him in that soft monotone.

At first Mr. Puffin was shy of coming too near the house. We arranged daily meetings with him on an old apple log that was awaiting the saw in the orchard. It became known as Mr. Puffin's Log.

Uncle Victor was with us night and morning. Though he now took many of his meals with us strangely enough my mother did not seem to mind. She did not mind when he sat late with my father sipping whisky-and-soda and talking about the old days.

For Mr. Puffin was thriving. He no longer carried his funny

little stump of a tail between his legs but held it jauntily erect. His fur glowed softly and his whiskers and eyebrows were like fine white bristles. *Hew, hew, hew* he mewed softly each night but now it was a greeting as he slid out of the grass and rubbed about our legs, dainty front paws treadling out his pleasure.

"The only thing that worries me," my father said, "is the birds." We had succeeded in attracting a nuthatch and a greater spotted woodpecker to our bird-table and he feared for their safety.

"They'll be all right," said Uncle Victor surprisingly. "Some cats are cruel, others aren't. Like humans. This one isn't."

We took this with a grain of salt but we could not deny Mr. Puffin the means of life. By the end of the summer he had taken to following any one of us about the garden all day like a dog, tail held high, throbbing his pleasure. My father noted with approval that the few mice he killed were dispatched with one skull-shattering blow from a dainty front paw. The fact that he did not toy with them seemed to bear out what Uncle Victor had said.

But he was still suspicious of the house and things like carpet-sweepers that made noises while the squeal of a mangle sent him flying for cover, tail fluffed out like a flue-brush.

"Take it gradually," Uncle Victor said. "Don't let him feel trapped. He's doing fine—his old tummy's as firm as a football."

Certainly Mr. Puffin was growing visibly each week. Once we had made him up a bed in an orange box in the garage he seemed disinclined to leave it. Stretched out in the darkness, his eyes glowing like hot green coals, he purred the night away.

But little by little Mr. Puffin became restless. We found him exploring other boxes, other sacks. When we took the plunge and moved his box into the kitchen, he came without a murmur. He sank into the Persian rug by the fire with a little whinnying sound and rubbed his chin against the fender in ecstasy.

Hew, hew, hew, he went as he moved about upstairs exploring cupboards and chests.

One day I got home from school to find my mother at the

door. She looked as if she didn't know whether to laugh or cry. " Come quietly," she said, " and come upstairs. Better be prepared for a shock."

She led the way to my father's dressing-room. Before I even got into the room I could hear the steady sound of purring. And there, in my father's wardrobe, bedded cosily down in the drawer where he kept his shirts . . .

" Oh, Mr. Puffin," I said.

" *Mrs.* Puffin," said my mother smiling, " And it explains a lot of things, especially her appetite. Including herself she's been eating for five. I only hope the joys of being a grandfather make up to your father for the loss of his shirts."

She need not have worried. My father was so little troubled he might have owned a hundred shirts, all of them silk. He summoned Uncle Victor at top speed. They crooned over the drawer while Mrs. Puffin stretched her paws at them and purred her pride in her new-born.

At first it was hard to share her pride. The kittens seemed nothing more than formless bundles of slick wet fur, as sightless and mindless as worms. But Mrs. Puffin loved them. She pinned each of them down in turn with a forepaw and washed them from stem to stern while they squealed and writhed. To wash you was her mark of supreme affection ; it showed that she loved you and wished to bring comfort. She would hold your fingers very firmly between her paws before washing all of them reflectively with a rough pink tongue.

As the kittens began to grow—the first of many many litters —we could see that her pride was not groundless. Tabby, tortoise-shell, coal-black and marmalade, like small furry, blue-eyed dolls, romping and tussling from morning to night.

" The great thing is to find good homes for them," Uncle Victor said. " We've got to organise a system. No use farming them out like ju-jubes. Only the best is good enough."

" We'll put a notice in Fisher's window," my mother said.

" And inspect every house personally," Uncle Victor added. " Homes with good gardens are what we want. Charles and I can divide it between us and compare notes."

"Lucy wants one," I said. "I heard her say so."

"The only thing I still worry about," my father said, "are the birds."

One Sunday soon after, when her kittens were fast asleep, Mrs. Puffin went for her morning stroll. Presently my mother came flying into the kitchen. "Scissors, quick," she said, "there a blackbird tangled in the pea-netting. The wretched thing will throttle itself if I don't cut it free."

"Mrs. Puffin went that way," I said with sinking heart.

"For heaven's sake," my father said, "She'll tear the poor brute to pieces if we don't hurry."

Helter-skelter we raced up the garden, my mother and father ahead, Uncle Victor and I following.

As we neared the kitchen garden my father groaned: "Too late . . . oh, too late. She's got it."

A familiar blob of black-and-white fur was squatting by the pea-netting. I had the impression that she had killed the bird and was eating it.

"*Watch !* " hissed Uncle Victor.

So we crept closer, and if I live to be a hundred I will never again see a sight like that. The blackbird was still tangled in the net, trapped by wings and claws, one bright yellow eye wary of our approach. But it was quite still, no longer struggling, for Mrs. Puffin sat beside it.

Mrs. Puffin was washing the backbird's head.

We had to remove her forcibly while we cut it free, she wanted so much to comfort it. I think she had suffered so much, compassion was a part of her.

"She's the nicest cat I've ever come across," my father said. "All her kittens shall have good homes."

"She's just an animal that had a chance," Uncle Victor said. "Give 'em a chance and there's so much good in all of them."

But this conversation came months later. They were sitting one on either side of the fire and my mother sat between them knitting. A bundle of marmalade fur with amber eyes was sporting with Uncle Victor's tie. A tabby as grave and sedate as a little French girl was asleep on my father's knee. Mrs. Puffin lay on the Persian rug, purring, green eyes fastened adoringly on the two most wonderful men in her world.

My father leaned across to the fire and tossed on a fresh billet of wood. "Well, she's settled now," he said. "She's got a home with us for life." A shower of red-gold sparks went sailing up the chimney from the last chunk of Mrs. Puffin's Log.

CHAPTER TWELVE

THE LAST OF SUMMER

What shall be the maiden's fate ?
Who shall be the maiden's mate ?

SIR WALTER SCOTT
The Lay of the Last Minstrel

THAT YEAR we took our summer holiday as usual, without thought. A hot summer it had been with no rain to comfort, the shaven grass of the tennis lawn as dry as coco-nut matting, the new peas coming small and tasteless from the pod.

My father had spent some happy days at Lord's, watching the Test Match and analysing each innings with the vicar. Along with a million other mothers of her generation my mother had braved the White Linen Sales, buying up enough sheets and Turkish towels and pillow-slips and drying-up cloths to equip a household ten times the size. From morning to night Lucy and Mrs. May waged their unrelenting war against dirt, polishing brass and oaken furniture until it shone like plate-glass. Uncle Victor still arrived unexpectedly to eat a schoolboy's breakfast and show us a new bird's egg.

Even the summer holiday followed the pattern of all summer holidays since time began. Nothing and nobody had changed. Not the good breakfasts of porridge and grilled fish in the dining-room of the private hotel, eaten in a silence broken only by the clearing of throats ; not the hasty scamper across the promenade, raincoats buttoned tightly over long one-piece bathing-suits—for it was " not done " to change on the beach.

Not the endless cups of morning coffee, the careful choice of coloured postcards (" ' X ' marks our room "), nor the dimly-lit hall of the hotel, its linoleum glinting with tiny grains of sand, dark coils of seaweed looped among the children's buckets and wooden spades.

It seemed that summer holidays had been like that since the days when I built my first laborious sand-castle on the beach at Seaford, crowning it in triumph, as did all we proud young heirs of the British Empire, with a paper Union Jack.

For if you went abroad, as my father said, you " never knew where you were." Going abroad, he said, was " all very well if you're taken that way but you can't beat England when all's said and done." Every summer in his youth he had spent his holidays abroad, but now, in his late fifties, these adventurings were done.

He no longer wanted to sleep in tiny whitewashed inns and eat food served in thick sharp sauces with good red wine on the side. He did not want to practise the French he had learned from Hugo's *French Simplified* on *le patron* or *la domestique*. He wanted mulligatawny soup, roast mutton and onion sauce and two vegetables followed by bread-and-butter pudding, whether the wind cut like a knife or the thermometer quivered in the eighties and he wanted them at one o'clock sharp, with the brassy notes of a gong to summon him. He wanted to relax with the latest Wodehouse and to take brisk walks for the good of his liver. He did not want accordion music echoing between the white walls of a Tyrolean town or the snap and crackle of a Sicilian puppet show. He wanted the Marine band, with pipe-clayed belts playing each afternoon on the promenade, " Devonshire teas " with cream and jam, the concert party on the pier in pierrot costumes, a soft landscape of white cliffs and blue-grey sea with children riding donkeys and Shetland ponies.

He wanted to be surprisingly informal in blazer and flannels, wearing for once a shirt with a soft collar (though not open at the neck), an ancient Trilby and white canvas shoes, with my mother wearing a cotton dress, a straw hat and flatter shoes though with gloves as usual. In the evening he wanted to hear the Palm Court orchestra play selections from Stephen Foster or see the repertory company on the pier struggling through a Noel Coward success of fifteen years before. He wanted England.

Now we had spent the five preceding summers in the same private hotel at Hythe, on the Kent coast, and the only difference between those years and the summer I am recalling—1938—was that we took our holiday with Aunt Emily and Uncle Hubert at Naini Tal, the private hotel they had bought on the Sussex coast at Eastbourne.

And it was family loyalty rather than anything else that sent us there for the hotel had not long been open but as my father said: " We Colliers must stick together."

The years had mellowed Uncle Hubert since that unforgettable and far-off Sunday when Uncle Victor had shot off his hat with a fir cone. Now retired, he was content to spend much of his day on the golf course in an old sports jacket patched with leather elbows, working to reduce his handicap. But time had wrought no change in Aunt Emily's fierce energy, like a new broom that would ever be sweeping clean and since her passion for organising things and people must always find some outlet Uncle Hubert had bought Naini Tal, so that he could find some peace on retirement. While she at sixty-five could find fulfilment in a seventeen-hour day and try with all her might to marry off her two daughters, Meg and Prudence, both of whom in this year had passed their fortieth birthday.

All her life, so far as I could understand, Aunt Emily had been wanting to make good marriages for her daughters ; she thought it would be an excellent thing if they could marry officers in the Indian Army and she saw it as her own shame that neither of them had ever showed much inclination to marry anybody at all. To her India was a land of mystery and romance, crystallising all the dreams she had nourished as a girl, and the result was an ambition for her daughters that neither of them shared and the purchase of this old-fashioned private hotel, with stained glass panels in its front door and a croquet lawn set about with monkey-puzzle trees, named after a Himalayan peak. Ever since I had known her Aunt Emily had been the same : a bustling little woman with an untamable shock of snow-white hair who spoke of herself either as " a breath of real fresh air " or " the little marvel." It was true that she had the energy of ten which sometimes proved too much for her family and nearly always for her staff but she had indomitable good humour and an unfailing belief in her own good sense which surmounted most obstacles. Staff, she confided in my mother, rattling away nineteen to the dozen, were " difficult " ; like her daughters, they did not know what was good for them. The cook had departed only a week earlier, remarking cryptically that the hotel gave her " the hab-dabs " and had only been replaced as we arrived.

I wonder what we should have done that summer if we had realised it would be almost the last holiday we should ever take together ? Of course we did not know. There was more anxiety beneath the surface, much talk of Dr. Benes, more readiness to listen to the news each night at nine o'clock. But no one doubted that it would come right somehow and we were prodigal of time. We bathed and made charabanc excursions to castles and abbeys, guide-books in hand, and we watched with fascination a strange comedy of manners taking place under our noses.

For after long endeavours and advertisements of special terms and hints to friends Aunt Emily had succeeded in luring two ex-officers of the Indian Army beneath her roof at the same time. If neither of them was quite what she had hoped for— for she had seen her prospective sons-in-law as bronzed and lean and born to the saddle—at least they were better than nothing. They were gentlemen and they had style. A girl could do worse.

Had either of the girls wanted to get married that might have been true. But my cousin Meg was a quiet retiring girl, shy sometimes to the point of sullenness, who had worked for a bookseller before the doctor prescribed sea air for her health ; she was happiest shut away in her room, reading, or taking long solitary walks on the cliffs, though she woke to life in my father's company and could discuss the classics with him for hours. Prudence was different altogether ; she ran much of the hotel with the briskness of a hospital matron, bred rabbits for pleasure and was only coaxed out of jodhpurs and a sweater with difficulty.

Yet both of them in their way I think were happy. If they would have been happier still married to the right man, they had outgrown the belief of Aunt Emily's generation that marriage to anyone was preferable to being " left on the shelf."

To make things worse both of the men on whom Aunt Emily had set her sights were confirmed bachelors. Major Jenkins, a gentle bespectacled veteran of the Accounts Department at Dehra Dun, had more interest in Etruscan art than marriage ; he was also a man to whom apology was the breath of life and my parents learned to duck quickly out of his way when he began to bare his soul on some imagined offence that he had caused to someone twenty years back. Colonel Dove, who did not spend more time than he could help with his brother officer, was a bald amiable little man who liked a feminine audience for his stories of regimental life ; he belonged to the old school who addressed any woman as " dear lady " as a matter of form.

But from the moment he had stepped inside the hotel eighteen months earlier and spoken like this to Meg, Aunt Emily was convinced that he had formed a secret attachment for her elder daughter. " Dove would be good for her," she declared. " He'd bring Meg out. As for Jenkins he needs a woman to make his mind up for him—someone like Prue."

" You're rushing things, old lady," Uncle Hubert warned, but he could not stop Aunt Emily. The chance she had awaited all these years was within an ace of being fulfilled. And her blood was up.

Her plan of campaign took the form of organised games in which we were sometimes expected to join for purposes of camouflage. Croquet on the lawn at four o'clock with the Rockingham tea-service as background could be very pleasant, though lent a certain tension by the reluctant presence of Major Jenkins, panama-hatted, as awkward and lanky as a stork, blinking with the eyes of a hurt spaniel through gold-rimmed spectacles, chewing his moustache with vexation as he muffed shot after shot. " I really am the world's worst duffer at this," he confided not without truth to Prudence, while my father relaxed, bored, on his mallet, and Aunt Emily, making a fourth, worked like a cheer-leader to keep things on the boil.

" Come on, partner—keen as mustard," she rallied my father as she scurried from hoop to hoop, her white hair fluffing like thistledown in the breeze.

Towards five o'clock my mother and I, returning up the drive from town, heard the snapping crack of broken glass. The game was over. Major Jenkins, stepping backwards to wring his hands over an extra poor shot, had put the business end of his croquet mallet through the drawing-room windows.

If the major had ever stood a chance with Prudence it was gone at that moment, shattered with the window-pane.

Not that she was a girl to scold or blame, being too down-to-earth, but the poor man was always one to apologise whether at fault or not. And now he had not only broken the window but as her partner, he would have it, let her down shamefully. For days thereafter Aunt Emily's hopes were high for the major was seeking Prudence's company at all hours—in the kitchen, where she supervised the lunches, down at the rabbit hutches, in the bedrooms as she dusted.

But not to pay court, oh, dear, no. To apologise six or a dozen times a day and strain her patience to snapping point. " I simply can't think," he would repeat again and again, " how I came to be so criminally careless."

And each time Prudence would retort more sharply, " Oh, bosh, Major. Accidents happen. Don't give it another thought."

She became blunter. She took to greeting him with upraised hand : " Look here, Major—enough said " before his mouth was even open. Meanwhile we went on bathing and taking charabanc rides and strolling on the pier and Aunt Emily went on trying.

" You're so short with him, Prue," she told her daughter. " I don't feel he'd be one to take liberties . . . there'd be no harm in trying a little harder to encourage him."

" I'm not trying to encourage him at all," said Prudence hotly. " So far as I'm concerned he's an outsize pain in the neck. I'm trying to shut him up."

Nothing was more plain than that despite Aunt Emily's

hopes the matter would never be brought to a head in our time there. Yet surprisingly the matter of Colonel Dove was.

With him it had always been more uphill work altogether. Aunt Emily had tried with all her might to find out how the colonel spent his afternoons; he was never available for a game of croquet and rarely took tea with the other guests in the drawing-room. Then a chance scrap of gossip from one of the maids put her on the right track. " Do you know what Dove does in the afternoons," she confided in my mother. " He *sleeps* if you ever heard of such a thing. It doesn't seem natural in a man of his age."

Of course my Uncle Hubert, who was much the same age, slept very soundly every afternoon from two to four, his face covered with a linen handkerchief, but his was a different case. He was not an eligible bachelor.

Each evening in the card room, an annexe of the main drawing-room fitted up with the same Benares brassware, pale ferns in pots and glass-fronted bookcases lined with Marie Corellis, Colonel Dove played bridge. But here was another problem. Neither Prudence nor Meg could play.

A genuine conflict of wills was there. The colonel resisted all Aunt Emily's efforts to lure him away from the bridge table. Even if he had been a willing captive, neither Prudence nor Meg wanted to hear his reminiscences of cantonment life in Jubbulpore. But Aunt Emily was not easily beaten. She had seen signs. A year ago the colonel had taken Meg to an Elgar recital at the local theatre and she was convinced that only shyness had prevented him from asking her again. He had offered her the shelter of his umbrella during a squall on the promenade—Meg had said so. And there was " dear lady "—clues enough for Aunt Emily when her mind was made up.

" He's such a fine military figure of a man," she said, " you can see he's been used to command."

He had spent most of his life in charge of supplies at base but Aunt Emily saw him as little less than a Bengal Lancer and she felt it in her bones that " if only Meg was less difficult Dove would ask her for a straight yes or no."

Now it happened that only a few nights before we left for home the colonel had dined earlier than usual. On his way out of the dining-room he paused as he always did for a few words with Aunt Emily and Uncle Hubert, who held a sort of informal court at their table near the door. As guests of honour at the same table we were witnesses to everything.

I had noticed that Meg, who sat beside me, had pushed her portion of spinach as far to one side of the plate as possible, though I thought my mother would have something to say if I did the same. And the colonel had noticed too. With a playful half smile he leaned across to Meg.

"Better be eating up our spinach," he said. "We shall be needing all our strength."

On that note he left and conversation would have become general again if Aunt Emily had not halted it like a conductor with upraised baton. "Well," she said into the silence, her face aglow with triumph, "we don't have to be very clever to draw our own conclusions from that."

"From what?" Meg wanted to know.

Aunt Emily looked incredulous. "You surely heard what Dove had to say for himself—and to you in particular?"

"Well, yes," Meg admitted, "if you want to know I thought he was jolly nosy. But good lord, Mother, don't go and make an issue of it."

Aunt Emily said no more until her daughters had left the table. But still, beneath the surface, she was bubbling with pent-up excitement. Then she said, "I think the next step is very plain. You're the girl's father, you should have a word with him. Catch him in the drawing-room while he has his coffee."

"But what about," Uncle Hubert rumbled. "Fellow makes a perfectly innocuous remark about spinach . . ."

"What *about*?" Aunt Emily's eyes went up as if to ask Heaven's protection. "Oh, *why* are men so slow? Does Dove have to propose at the table before you can take his meaning? Ask yourself a simple question—why else should Meg be needing all her strength if she hadn't got to get a trousseau together and a hundred and one other things ? What with dressmakers and all the rest I know it wore your little marvel out and you know Meg's never been strong."

"You're rushing things, old lady," said Uncle Hubert, thoroughly alarmed. "You can't just take a man up on the slightest word . . ."

But Aunt Emily was inflexible. "If you won't protect your daughter's interests," she said coldly, "I will."

It was not until the next night that Aunt Emily managed to waylay Colonel Dove, though we never heard the actual words spoken between them. Taking our coffee in the far corner of the drawing-room we could see only the expression on their faces, but that was enough. To study the colonel's face changing through polite interest to puzzled disbelief and finally to a kind of blank despair told us more plainly than any words the outcome of the conversation.

"How did you put it to him ? " my father twinkled, when Aunt Emily rejoined us, brimming with satisfaction.

"I think I put it very nicely," Aunt Emily said reflectively. "Certainly not in a way that would give offence. I said that of course I was against rushing things but we did feel it was time we all got to know one another better. I said from now on we wanted him to think of himself as just one of the family and to feel free to take his meals with us. It can't be very nice for him, after all, sitting alone like that."

"Now look here," Uncle Hubert exploded, " I've got nothing against the fellow but if you think I want his memories of Jubbulpore dished up with every meal . . ."

"Hubert," said Aunt Emily at her most energetic, " I've never heard of anything so selfish. For Meg's sake we must be prepared to make small sacrifices and if you're going to start being difficult . . ."

But later over cigars my father found it in him to console Uncle Hubert. " I shouldn't worry if I were you," he murmured, " I don't think it occurred to Emily, but the colonel might start being difficult too."

He had noticed what Uncle Hubert had not ; that the colonel

was not playing bridge that night. We looked for him but he was nowhere to be seen.

. . .

"Do you remember Dove," wrote Aunt Emily some time after in one of the twelve-page dispatches she sent to members of her family twice a year, " the colonel who was staying here at the same time as you, who we all thought was so keen to make a go of it with Meg ? Believe it or not, he got cold feet ! He went on a business trip to town last month then wrote asking for all his things to be sent on to the —— Club as he now had to stay on in town indefinitely. But obviously he had this whole thing planned for his trunks were packed and ready—fancy leading Meg to expect so much and then to behave so shabbily, though she is being very good about it all. . . ."

CHAPTER THIRTEEN

TO MEET THE KING

---

*To be honest, to be kind—to earn a little
and to spend a little less, to make upon the
whole a family happier for his presence . . .
here is a task for all that a man has of
fortitude and delicacy*

ROBERT LOUIS STEVENSON
Across the Plains

A LETTER for my father arrived on the breakfast table. But it was
no ordinary letter that came this summer morning. From the
ivory tint of the envelope, the rich seal embossed on its flap,
we could tell that.

And the wording on the tall sheet of creamy paper—it needed
a flourish of silver trumpets and a herald's proclamation to do
it justice.

George the Sixth by the Grace of God of Great Britain,
Ireland and the British Dominions beyond the Seas, King,
Defender of the Faith . . . to our trusty and well-beloved
Charles Aubrey Collier Esquire, Greeting . . . Whereas We
have thought fit to nominate and appoint you to be a Member
of the Civil Division of Our Said Most Excellent Order of the
British Empire. . . .

"Oh, Charles," my mother said, the teapot hovering in
space, "the M.B.E. . . . But you never said . . . not one
word . . ."

"Well," my father admitted, so close to his plate you might have thought his sight was failing, "I knew something was in the wind, of course . . . but it hardly seemed decent to make a song and dance about it. I mean, think of all the poor devils who've deserved it more than I."

"To tell your wife," said my mother, her eyes shining with pride and love, "is to make a song and dance about it. Whatever next I'd like to know. And here it says Morning Dress Will Be Worn, but it doesn't say anything about taking guests so does that mean I can't even see you wearing morning dress to order?"

But her mind was as quick as ever so that before my father could even answer she was seeing the way. "But yes, I can though—because you'll have to hire it and bring it home. So then you'll change here and travel up . . ."

"*No!*" said my father suddenly, his voice so strangled just then that imprisonment or worse might have been facing him, "My dear, *no*. I'm sorry, but I can't. I just couldn't walk through the village dressed like that and look people in the face. I mean, what would they think?"

"But Charles," my mother reasoned, sweet as honey from the hive, "why shouldn't you look them in the face? You've done nothing *wrong*. You're going to meet the King. He's going to decorate you."

My father blew his nose with force and his voice was riding a wind. "Yes," he said, "I know. And don't think I don't realise it's an honour . . . a very great honour.

"But do try and see . . . it's for the department as a whole, not me . . . I suppose I've been there so long I'm a kind of symbol. It wouldn't be right if I was to—to *dress up* as if I was advertising a circus and parade through the village. We'll have a little dinner and a theatre later on, I promise . . . but if *that* day isn't just like any other day it wouldn't seem right."

Now if any circus on earth ever sent out the big drum and the clowns to parade the streets led by a sober and dignified Englishman in morning dress I have yet to hear of it. But that

was my father for you. Nothing my mother and I said—for
with a fond notion that he might have to wear a sword I was
specially eager—could budge him.

On that day everything must be normal and uneventful.
He didn't even want to think that other people were thinking
about it; it would put him off his stride. Indeed, it would probably even embarrass him.

But he was not to be let off so lightly. There was a month
to go before the investiture was held at St. James's Palace.
Guests were not invited in those days and though he could stop
my mother and me and almost everyone save the anonymous
taxi-driver who carried him from the outfitters from seeing him
in morning dress he could not stop us talking.

So the news spread across the valley.

First Lucy and Mrs. May. Then Mr. May. The vicar.
Sparrow, the butcher, with his blue-and-white apron and Fisher,
the newsagent, with his bushy walrus moustache. All smiling.
All anxious to shake my father by the hand. All saying, in
different tones and accents, the same thing: " Very nice to
hear your news, sir. . . ."

Old Mr. Collier was going to meet the King.

" You show 'em, guv'nor," said an old crony of Mr. Wade's,
meeting my father in the lane.

At first my father was indignant. " You've been *telling*
people," he accused my mother, as if he had caught her red-
handed in some crime. Yet when my mother did not deny it
he was taken aback. And when she said that far from being
ashamed of it she *wanted* people to know, that she had never
been more proud of him and she thought he deserved some
credit after serving his country for forty years, my father was
ready to change the whole subject quicker than fire will flash.

Only he muttered something about " not playing the game "
but that was all.

Yet from then on there was a change and we were quick to
notice it.

For by now my father had had time to think about it. And
he had become proud. Not proud in the sense of his nose held

high but proud in the knowledge of a job well done. You see, those forty years embraced more than the work he had done for the Government. In a way the decoration symbolised a milestone in his life. Forty years, and he and my mother could look into one another's eyes and know more often than not that there was no need for words. Forty years, and for fifteen of them the house had stood above the valley staunch against rain and wind and the earth that lay about it had been made fertile through his labour. Forty years, and his family saw him as a rock and he had brought happiness to those about him and kept faith and betrayed no trust.

How many of us could say as much?

So now when congratulations were heaped upon him and the first writhing embarrassment was past he had learned to smile, still colouring a little, and say, " Well, you're very kind, you know . . . but really it's for my department. . . ."

But he had his way in that when the great day dawned everything was much as always. I know that he set off by his usual train though perhaps he was a shade pale that morning and holding himself more stiffly than usual as he went through the front gate.

After that, all was confusion in my father's mind. First, of course, the journey to Moss Bros. in Covent Garden and the fitting of the morning dress : black frock-coat and striped trousers, dove-grey waistcoat and gloves, grey silk topper. Then they called a taxi and hastily my father was smuggled into it, on his way to St. James's Palace.

And I know it was a day when the sun shone brightly so that as the men about to be decorated—and all of them, I don't doubt, as nervous as my father—lined up in the blue-and-gold Throne Room the military band was playing on the lawn outside. So as they advanced, one by one, with the voice of the Lord Chamberlain tolling out their names, it was to the faint strains of Gilbert and Sullivan that my father met his King and the cherry-coloured ribbon with the silver edging was pinned to his left breast.

" And . . . well," he said afterwards, striving to take hold

on some memory that would light up the whole scene for us,
" We . . . shook hands, you know . . . and he was very
kind . . ."

" But didn't the King say anything ? " my mother wanted to
know.

Oh, yes, my father had to admit, the King had said something
—but what he said had now quite escaped him. A kindly word
or two—but his brain had been too frozen with the honour of
the moment to really take it in.

" After all," he explained, " there was no reason why he
should have said anything in particular to *me* . . . I was there
for the department really."

Though he added, " But he'll be a good King, you know—
he's a fine young fellow. And I think we shall have need of
him."

Strange then that he should have remembered more of what
happened afterwards than of the ceremony itself but this is the
story that he told :

When he had returned to Moss Bros. and changed out of
morning dress it was past noon. And standing on the pavement
in the brilliant sunshine he felt in urgent need of something that
he had rarely ever craved at that time of day.

And that was a stiff drink for his knees were trembling
a little and he knew for the first time what an ordeal this had
been.

But this was Covent Garden Market, a district he did not
know well, so taking pot-luck he pushed through the door of
the nearest pub.

Not the right pub—he saw that at a glance. It was hot,
crowded and noisy, smelling of bitter beer and trodden vegetables,
packed out with market workers in white mufflers and cloth caps,
so that the sudden entry of an elderly man in a dark suit, with
spats, carrying a cane, took them, as you might say, unawares.
Many men might have turned on their heels at once and sought
other company but my father was a gentleman. He would hurt
no one's feelings deliberately.

So to the bar he went and ordered a large brandy and soda

and it was when he was sitting at a scrubbed table sipping it that he caught the woman's eye.

She was an old flower-seller, my father said, who had come to the market that morning for fresh blooms. Now, with bunches of gladioli stacked about her, she was consoling herself with a pint of stout. An old black battered hat was set askew on her grey head. Her face was red, her eyes were moist and merry and her laugh was Cockney—warm and living, ribald, straight from the belly.

They exchanged a few words about the weather and the heat and something about my father sitting there, hot and correct in his business suit, sipping brandy with a rose in his buttonhole, must have struck some chord of sympathy.

For a family man, hard-working these forty years, for one of God's creatures ? I don't know—but suddenly she closed one eye in a great wicked bibulous wink.

" What a life, dear, eh ? " her voice came wheezing. "And all for a crust."

It tickled my father, that, to picture this morning's strange contrasts : the young King and the old flower-seller. Often in later years, when things went awry, the ghost of a smile lit his face as it came back to him and he would murmur, " What a life, dear, eh . . . and all for a crust."

.   .   .

It is strange that you can forget so many things and yet hold a picture of a woman's hands that have been still all these years.

Lucy's hands were busy at the kitchen-sink that Sunday morning, red and toil-worn as always, yet a miracle of deftness and order when it came to peeling King Edward potatoes and stringing runner beans and setting knobs of dripping on a saddle of mutton to make it crisp and sweet.

It was so hot that it was warm cotton wool you were trying to breathe and I had been to the kitchen at least twice for a glass of my mother's home-made ginger beer. And not ordinarily welcome at such a time on a Sunday but this morning my mother had no heart to bustle me out.

There was that Sunday smell the kitchen always had of roasting meat and polish and washing-soda and wood scrubbed white and the cool green odour of freshly-picked vegetables. My father was bringing them from the kitchen-garden this morning, but walking slowly like a much older man, with Mrs. Puffin trotting dog-like at his heels.

You could hear the traffic far away on the main road and the bees from the lavender beds where the kittens were playing, yet all was so quiet you could hear the beating of your heart.

When Uncle Victor looked in on his way home he came in quietly by the french windows, as if ashamed of coming, but my father went in and poured him sherry without a word and without a word Uncle Victor took it.

And all the time I was watching Lucy's hands. Brisk and sure, and only faltering for a second now and then as if she were listening for something. Yet somehow in the determined briskness of the red swollen fingers, the nails cracked and split, you sensed the fears and doubts that all women knew that day, though their fingers went on working.

The radio crackled into life from the drawing-room but I did not move. I stayed in the kitchen with my mother and Lucy and together we heard a man speak. An old tired man, his voice cracking with strain, who spoke only one sentence we heard . . . " consequently this country is at war with Germany."

Lucy was looking out of the window, across the tennis-lawn. I could not see her face. When that last sentence came her hands clenched tight on the taps above the sink and held on. And I saw the red knuckles blanch to white.

" Oh, m'm," she said presently, turning to my mother with a stone in her throat. " Oh, m'm, I am sorry."

God be with you, dear Lucy. It was almost as if you knew.

CHAPTER FOURTEEN

WINTER IN THE HEART

Childhood is the kingdom where nobody dies
EDNA ST. VINCENT MILLAY

IT WAS all over so quickly that it seemed a matter of days. And though it was months, years even, before we saw the outcome, it was within days that the pattern was made plain.

Within days we knew that my father had to go away—to fight his war, at the age of sixty, in the cold north-coast town where his department was to be evacuated. My father said with the optimism that was so much part of him that it would " all be over by Christmas " but the question was in our minds unspoken : would he ever sleep beneath this roof again ?

Within days I was back at school, studying for the Cambridge University Higher Schools Certificate, but burdened now by a portable boxed gas-mask, deep in one of the air-raid shelters that scarred the school grounds for much of each day.

All over, now, the tennis and the tea-parties. No more lighting two fires of a morning, no more polishing shoes for the sake of it. Both coal and polish were too scarce, as scarce as time. When Lucy was too old to come my mother needed that time to polish and light the one small fire, to search for cat's meat and eggs to put in water-glass and powdered milk and margarine, and Mrs. May helped out whenever she could.

Our world was changing.

For the better in many ways, I will not deny. How often

I had thought contemptuously of Mr. Graveney that summer afternoon at the tennis-party . . . "very sound this man, Chamberlain . . . not the type to be bamboozled by dictators." Of Mr. Graveney and all his kind whose complacency and short-sightedness, as I thought then, had brought us to this. But now, Mr. Graveney, who was my father's age, was out night after night in bitter weather with an air-raid warden's white helmet—"standing by," he said, "just standing by." Mr. Dyne of the Colonial Office, also in his sixties, was crawling on his stomach through ditches, leading his little troop of Home Guards on manœuvres, though they had more spades and hedging tools than rifles for weapons in the breathless week of Dunkirk.

The fighter planes snarled and spun and dived over our valley, glinting in the sunlight, while all the Mr. Graveneys stood by.

Of course the women had more to yield. So many old unchallenged standards had to go by the board that it cannot have been easy for almost all that winter they held out, watching Mrs. Colonel Frensham, as she was known, the wife of the biggest landowner in those parts.

But there came a day when the colonel's lady walked into the village wearing not a costume and a fur stole but an old tweed top-coat that must have been outdated in King George V's time. Only a faded old scarf that had seen better days graced her head. Not only was she placing her own orders; she was carrying home her groceries in a wicker basket. Moving from shop to shop, she nodded and smiled graciously to those who had never merited a nod before.

And suddenly the mood changed. For the first time in all my life the village became shabbily proud. A smile was an introduction. Total strangers, become boon friends in a queue for salt cod, went home to trade recipes over coffee made from powdered milk.

So much that was good had gone with it but the whole façade of our world had crumbled. Now it was the world that Lucy and her kind had lived by: what a man put into life, not what he put into the bank.

Then the bombs began to fall.

Night after night the house shuddered and shook as the bombers passed on their way to London and behind the thick fusty black-out curtains my mother knitted socks and pullovers and wrote endless letters to my father. Every day he wrote back.

News came of old friends. For a whole year they did not tell Aunt Helen Victoria that the war was on. They thought the shock would kill her. Instead she bucked up enormously and joined Aunt Kate knitting for the Navy ; it put years on her life. Uncle Victor volunteered for the Home Guard once a week and once a week with due courtesy they turned him down. At seventy-five he had to be satisfied with putting out incendiary bombs at three a.m. and turning his entire garden over to cabbages. He groused bitterly over Gort's handling of the B.E.F., threatening not to have his hair cut until the Allies had reached Berlin.

Cousin Jasmine had so far forgotten the Peace Pledge Union that she made part of an anti-aircraft guncrew on the outskirts of London. Cousin Andrew had turned aside from our radio for there were tanks to take to pieces and reassemble now on a cold Scottish moor.

Slowly our house grew shabbier. Walls and woodwork cracked with the pounding of the guns and were not patched up. The roof tiles seeped water. The tennis-lawn was spongy with moss, and rank grass tangled the rose garden and the lavender beds. But Mr. May was a fireman now, far away in Cambridge, and nothing could be done.

And my father. He came south on leave in time for the last great raid on London—older, greyer, suddenly haggard-looking with the strain of a fourteen-hour day and food he did not like and chilly respectable lodgings and above all, loneliness.

That night the bombers set all London on fire and turned the moon to blood. Three canisters of incendiaries landed by a miracle not on the house but on the tennis-lawn and in the morning you could scarcely see where the lawn had been. Only thousands of sickly-white patches that had stained the grass, ploughing wicked little holes in the cherished turf.

My father went out to see it and came back struggling with something inside himself. "Well," he said at last, "if they'll do that, this is war."

You had to laugh then but with kindness, for all his twenty years of labour had gone, gone for nothing. He only went out once again to the garden before he journeyed back, standing a long time in the twilight alone.

In that quiet garden, amid the fading light, I think he saw the end of all that he would do.

.　　　.　　　.

Word came from my mother that my father was desperately ill. Two years had passed and I had gone to war with the R.A.F. "If he'd retire," she said, "there might be some hope. But I can't make him . . . he's got this idea . . . and it all seems so silly." She began to cry.

He had come south to see a specialist and I tried to persuade him. "I'll pack up soon, old chap," he said. "There's just something I've got to do first."

But it is shocking to see a man who has been the centre of your universe going to pieces before your eyes : the skin yellow and drawn tight over the cheek-bones, the pupils of the eyes dilated, the lips ashen and dry.

He worked for three more months before collapsing. But he gave me to understand he was satisfied. The mysterious thing that he had to accomplish had been done.

And remembering all that he had taught me I found myself trying to be cool, to be practical, to prepare for a burden heavier than I had ever shouldered in the years that were gone. The maples were turning to scarlet again when he came home to die. But he did not know it.

"Look after your mother," he said once. "She deserves only the best you can do for her."

But he lingered.

Nine months he lingered in the big bedroom upstairs with

its china ewers and its grey-green walnut. He fought to keep hold on life and the lilac he loved came again and sometimes from the depths of coma he wanted to hear the church bells that could ring only as a signal for invasion. Nine months while my mother tended him alone, with only a district nurse to do the unmentionable things that had to be done.

And what the pain did to him in those months is nothing that you can write about but there were times when the sense of pain seemed to tear the house apart.

The final news came to me too late. By the time I reached home it was night and he had been gone two hours.

There is a sense of anti-climax here. You enter a room on tiptoe as if it was a stranger's room and this man, lying so still with the cheeks like pale moulded wax, is your father. This man who taught you not to lie, to honour women, who guided your footsteps as you learned to walk on the drive down there, has slipped from you, has gone before you can say good-bye. You could bite your lips until the blood came because now it will always be too late.

You can only hold him tight to you, feeling his bristles cutting into your cheeks, seeing his little hands so neat upon the coverlet, the grief coming out of you slowly and in spasms, with great anguish, as a child is born.

.   .   .

"Bloody shame, I call it," said an old countryman Lucy had known. "Great little English gentleman he was, too. We'll not see many more like him in our time."

.   .   .

My mother sat as still as a stone figure and stared across polished brass and woodwork to the ruined garden.

"So that's the end of it," she said, her mouth ugly, "the end of all he worked for."

"We knew it was coming," I said.

My mother turned on me like an animal. "Coming?" she said, "coming like that? Were you with him at the last to know what it was like—or even why it happened? The house is ours now, you know—he put it off and put it off but it's ours now—and as much as anything he died for that."

I said stupidly, my mouth open: "But it was always ours."

"That's what you thought," said my mother, "that's what he wanted you to think. Now see this," and she handed me something I could make no sense of at first but it was a building society pass-book. "You can see the last payment, can't you? Nine months ago and he worked on like that, knowing he was ill, to make it. Not even admitting he was ill in case they retired him. He did it for us and the house is ours now and I hope you'll think it's worth it. All I wish now is that I'd never set eyes on it . . . he loved it but it destroyed him in the end. . . ."

To-morrow she would not mean it. But it hurt then.

.   .   .

Yet how would my mother have felt if she had known that in the end I stayed?

For when she too went and the pain of that day was past I knew that my life was here. The blood of them all, my family and my friends, moved in my veins still and their bones and sinews were the framework of this house.

For them I dug with spade and fork and pick, restoring a ruined garden. For them I worked long hours to make this house the symbol of the shining truths they taught me.

It was they who showed me the better way, above the fumblings and graspings of greed. They taught me to see the world as a child and to preserve that wonder in freshness until the grave.

And in teaching me these things they were more clever than they knew. They became immortal, living on within these walls, for none of them are dead. No matter what the world may say, they are not dead.

Is Lucy dead, with her warm brown eyes and her red, work-scarred hands, the hands that clenched in sympathy when our world was ending, that bathed me before I had even learned to walk? But how dead when for me she lives each morning at dawn with the click of a light-switch in the kitchen and the start of a new day ?

Is Suzanne dead, her hair like ripe wheat and her lips upturned to mine in the darkness of our sanctuary, who took my hand in the knowledge that a man will fight for what he loves ? How can she ever die when that truth is inside me, living in a house founded on love ?

Did Uncle Victor die at last ? But as God is our Father he is down there now, hammering on the door with his old ash stick, to talk till nightfall about old books and old breakfasts, and to win his way back into my mother's heart with his tenderness for " Mrs. Puffin." And I see his head thrown back in laughter and pride, watching the boy he loved sitting as one with the gipsies and farmers in the bar of an enchanted inn, and his iron grip is about my waist as he plucks me from death in the fast-flowing river.

And what of you, my father ? I know you are alive for every room is quick with your presence : it lies like a sudden stillness upon the garden that you loved. And I think you knew, even that night that you sat beside my bed, that you had charted my destiny in the span of a sentence.

For it was you, wasn't it, who taught me to see God in this garden, to treasure the trust of a child or an animal, and what went to make " a gentleman." From you I learned that a man can forget the world if he has his soul in safe keeping, that to do our best is all that most of us can hope for, that beside the love of a good woman or the comfort of a firm friend, all the gold in the world is ashes.

And you taught me because you knew I would stay, for this was the vision that you saw.

Isn't this the future you planned, my father who was all things to me, a dream you dreamed by a small boy's bedside to fulfil in death in a house called memory when the maples were scarlet upon the hill ?

THE END